Assembling the Forest

Once the physical attributes and design potential of a new community forest area have been assessed, extensive attention must be given to the pattern of existing land-ownership and the opportunities and constraints which it presents. There is no question of requiring anyone to plant trees but much might be done in open discussion to ensure that individual intentions fit into a strategy which will yield an eventual forest which is much more than the sum of its parts. The views of all landowners, whether private individuals, corporate bodies or public institutions are vitally important and must be ascertained. Means must be found for describing a design strategy as it builds up so that key locations are identified and options explored in a way which remains indicative and as flexible as possible. There can be no imposed solutions. **The best community forests established in the closing years of this century will be those which combine a tough minimal framework with opportunism.** There are several options available to create this framework.

a   **Creating or maintaining a strong enclosure pattern of hedgerows, trees and small woods helps to integrate larger areas of woodland established in the future.** These patterns may be strong enough to over ride minor landforms. In many urban fringe areas earlier woodland and hedgerow patterns have broken down and some strengthening and re-establishment is neccessary. Such patterns have a useful function as wildlife corridors, assisting colonisation of any newly planted areas.

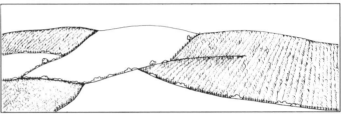

3a. A landscape where the previously strong hedgerow pattern has disintegrated.

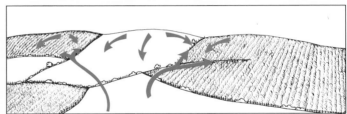

b. An analysis reveals the landform which coincides with some of the former enclosure pattern, and a medium to small scale.

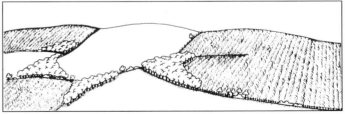

c. Reinstatement of the enclosure pattern together with small copses planted to respond to landform created a stronger landscape structure at the correct scale.

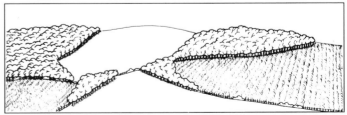

d. At some later date it is possible to plant complete fields which instantly become linked into the re-established pattern.

b. **In flatter or gently rolling landscapes the edges of woodlands are more important, particularly in the way they react together to create and enclose space, than the shapes of woods seen in plan.** In open landscapes straight woodland edges look artificial, even when following former field boundaries. Straight edges cutting across even subtle landform have disruptive effects. Woodland margins should be shaped in plan to respond to land form in a minor way, and so make interlock possible when adjacent ground is planted. It is also possible, through the devices of coalescence and overlap, to have small woodlands composed together to create enclosure and make the landscape seem more wooded than it really is.

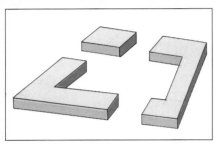

4a. A diagrammatic view of woodland planted following former field.

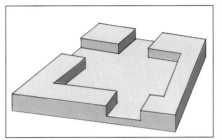

b. Additional woodland planted at a later date abuts the older woods. The geometric age-class boundary will persist through the life of the two areas.

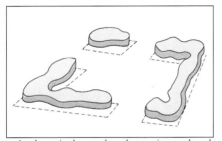

c. An alternative layout where the margins are shaped in plan to respond to subtle changes in landform.

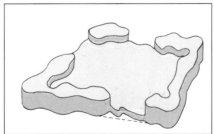

d. The infilled planting interlocks with earlier woodland and geometry is eliminated.

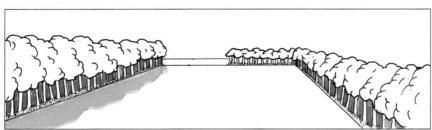

5a. The view into the space created by planting to a geometric plan along field margins. The regularity is maintained and exaggerated.

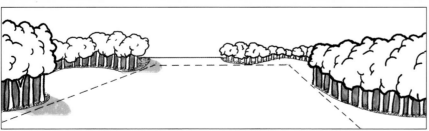

b. Planting to a more flowing edge shape within the boundary of the original planting achieves a more natural shape and better unity through interlock with the open space.

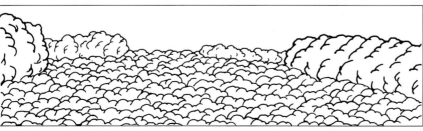

c. The later infill planting automatically interlocks with the established woodland edge shapes.

COMMUNITY WOODLAND DESIGN

GUIDELINES

LONDON : HMSO

i

COMMUNITY WOODLAND DESIGN GUIDELINES

FOREWORD

© *Crown copyright 1991*
First published 1991

ISBN 0 11 710300 4
Printed in the UK for HMSO
Dd 293229 11/91 C50

Enquiries relating to this publication should be addressed to:
The Technical Publications Officer,
Forestry Commission,
Forest Research Station,
Alice Holt Lodge,
Wrecclesham,
Farnham,
Surrey
GU10 4LH

FOREWORD

A great deal has happened since we said in July 1985, in the context of our broadleaved woodland policy statement, that we wished to see woodlands "established in areas where they are scarce, including areas on the periphery of towns and cities".

Throughout Britain there has been a growing recognition of the valuable part that trees can play in the lives of an essentially urban population by enclosing the built environment in a green envelope. Most conspicuous have been the initiatives launched to encourage the establishment of a dozen community forests in England, the imaginative project for a major new forest in the English Midlands and the equivalent in the Central Lowlands of Scotland.

These design guidelines have been prepared by Simon Bell, the Forestry Commission's Senior Landscape Architect, drawing on practical experience in the Commission going back over a quarter of a century under the wide tutelage of Dame Sylvia Crowe, Clifford Tandy and Gordon Patterson, successive landscape consultants to the Commission. The development of the guidelines has also been influenced by fruitful discussion with many people working in the field.

As a Forestry Minister, I warmly welcome this publication which I am sure will prove of great value not only to people thinking about the development of new woodlands, but to those who are managing existing woodlands for the direct pleasure of visitors.

THE BARONESS TRUMPINGTON
Minister of State
Ministry of Agriculture, Fisheries and Food

COMMUNITY WOODLAND DESIGN GUIDELINES

1. INTRODUCTION

There is a substantial body of experience in Britain in the design of woodlands and the incorporation of recreation and wildlife conservation areas within them. Drawing on this experience, new multipurpose forests near urban areas can be created with some confidence. We can also learn from the well established urban fringe forests in other countries, notably Holland and Germany. These give useful pointers as to what design features are likely to be most successful, and an indication of how our own forests may look when mature.

Most community woodlands and forests in Britain will differ from those in some other European countries in that the local community will not "own" the forest, except to the extent that part of the land in question may be owned by the public authorities. They will be made up of land in many different ownerships, and owners will have their own objectives for their own particular woodlands. This will of itself throw up unusual challenges for woodland design.

The information in this booklet will be of assistance to anyone involved in planning, designing and managing community woodlands. Sections 2 - 4 are primarily aimed at those requiring an overview of an entire community forest area, such as planners, landscape architects and the larger landowners. Section 5 deals with principles of visual design and sections 6 - 10 are particularly relevant to the owners and managers of individual woodland areas, both existing and proposed, which might contribute to a community forest. Farmers, foresters, mineral extractors and utility engineers, as well as planners, will find these chapters useful.

2. THE WOODLAND DESIGN PROCESS

Woodland design is about achieving a balance between site requirements, function and aesthetics. It should reflect and enhance the best natural qualities of the landscape, incorporate natural features and detail, and reduce visual intrusion and eyesores as far as possible. It should assist in the development of a wide range of habitats, recreational opportunities and meet the operational needs of efficient woodland management.

Appraisal Survey

Design should begin with the appraisal of the major influences at work in the existing landscape. These include:

- the regional landscape context;
- physical conditions - geology, soil types, topography and exposure;
- existing areas of ecological importance especially woodland;
- roads, other access routes.

Sensitivity and character of the existing landscape are assessed, and aesthetic problems identified. Information is needed on what people want.

Site appraisal identifies constraints and opportunities, within which the plan for creating a community forest can be developed. This must provide a framework to guide individual initiatives, yet be flexible enough to accommodate changing demands and circumstances. A design concept is now arrived at, derived from the broad landscape and other influences and a desired overall balance of woodland and open ground.

Useful information on this aspect of design is contained in "Advice Manual for the Preparation of a Community Forest Plan", Countryside Commission CCP 271.

Design Techniques

The site appraisal involves recording and analysis of landform. This requires contour maps and photographs of perspective views. The latter are particularly useful when taken from known and important viewpoints. Landform is best recorded as visual forces, shown running down spurs and ridges and up hollows and concavities. (For a full statement of this technique see Section 5.)

Once landform and other factors are identified, the layout of woodland and open space, and the precise requirements of individual features, can be designed in detail. The steps in this process are:

- get the broad shapes right;
- decide the form of the external woodland margins;
- define open spaces within the forest; shapes and timing of felling; species patterns; detailed edge treatments and treatment of special sites.

Design of woodland is best done at a scale of 1 : 10 000 or 1 : 5000, rather than the scales of 1 : 1250 or 1 : 200 often used by designers. A scale of 1 : 500 is commonly used for recreation site design.

Designs should be drawn on perspectives, usually photocopies from perspective photographs taken from key viewpoints, using crayon or felt-tip pen. Aerial perspectives are also useful: drawn sections and elevations much less so. Perspective views are important even in flat areas.

The designs have to take into account the effects of tree growth and future management. The development of new woodland can be demonstrated via accurate sketches on photographic perspectives. This is particularly important if it is to be integrated with or among existing woodland, some of which will be subject to felling. It is essential to be able to predict what an area will look like, in shape and scale, before any felling is actually carried out; mistakes can take a very long time to rectify. If available, topographic modelling on computer is very helpful especially at the trial-and-error stage of design.

Drawings and panoramic photographs are the best means of presenting and displaying the design, the various alternatives being shown on transparent overlays. The chosen design must then be transferred accurately to a contour map to enable it to be set out correctly on the ground.

Perspective drawings of the final design are particularly helpful in public consultation, conveying information on proposals much more readily than by maps. They can be sited at viewpoints, so that people can see and understand what is going on as time progresses. They are also valuable in monitoring and keeping the progress of the design up to date, and recording any changes which may occur during implementation.

1. Illustrations of how woodland is expected to look are best carried out on photocopies of panoramic photographs. Here felt-tip pens have been used to show different species and different ages of trees in a realistic way.

Implementation and Management

Marking the design layout on the ground can be done in a variety of ways. One of the best is to survey in points along the margin of shapes, identify these by conspicuous pegs and coloured streamers; then check the shapes from various viewpoints, amending if necessary.

How the design is actually implemented by planting and by subsequent management will vary greatly depending on who owns and manages the site.

3. LANDSCAPE ASSESSMENT AND PLANNING

Landscape assessment and planning will be an important part of the development of a community woodland.

Landscape Character

Understanding the landscape character of a potential community forest area is necessary so that the design of new woodland reinforces it, takes inspiration from it and helps to strengthen the local sense of place. Assessment of landscape character must not be a statistical description in terms of numbers of elements. It must avoid subjectivity as far as possible. A rational, professional approach is necessary, based on a descriptive vocabularly. The visual design principles outlined in section 5 will help in analysis of the landscape and in assessing its character.

In some areas the degree of relief and its scale will be significant. More relief means more interest, longer views and straightforward cues for design; it also means that dilapidation is less easy to hide and poor design is more obvious.

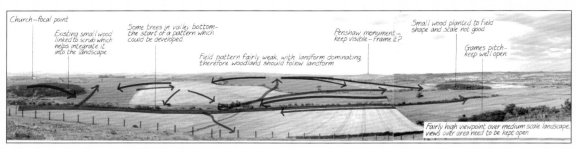

2. The landscape character may be assessed from a number of viewpoints, and the particular features recorded on an overlay. This acts as an aide-memoire when carrying out later work.

c. **Where landform is more pronounced, or where a forest area will be seen from vantage points so that much is in view at once, woodland shapes must be designed to follow landform and to create strong interlock between the planted area and the open ground.** Well designed margins help to avoid the geometric butt-joint, which will otherwise occur when adjacent areas have very different ages of trees. In such landscapes the main problem is to achieve an appropriate scale. It will often not be possible to find ownership units which coincide with landform units, or of the right scale, especially near skylines. The problems should be discussed with landown-ers. It may be possible to plant appropriately sized areas, or across joint boundaries. If not, smaller woods can be designed to give the appearance of larger scale through the use of overlap, interlock, coalescence and nearness. These techniques are described in detail below.

A woodland structure with a strong relationship to landform and in scale with the landscape enables the forest to grow and develop without passing through a phase when it looks chaotic. In some agricultural areas well-intentioned plantings of small woods in field corners have created intrusive effects because the enclosure pattern has broken down and there is nothing to tie such small–scale woods into the landscape.

The desirable balance between woodland and open ground in a new community forest will affect the preference of areas to plant. The current concept of community forests, for example, suggests that roughly one-third of the designated area should eventually be under trees, so there will still be large areas of open space. Some of these will be roads, corridors for services, land for houses and industry but more will be open ground of one sort or another. The preferred balance and scale of the open ground between areas of woodland should be considered at an early stage, for each character type and landscape unit.

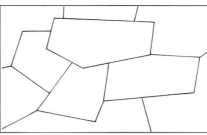

6a. Four areas of land under different ownerships which may become available for planting at different times.

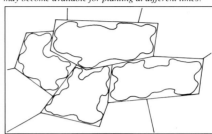

b. A pattern of layouts within each ownership unit which could each be capable of being planted without compromising the eventual unified pattern of the whole.

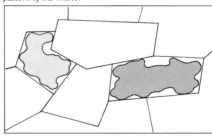

c. Phase one: two owners decide to plant their areas using the layouts from (b.)

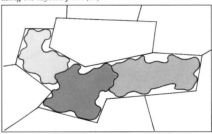

d. At a later date a third owner plants his area. This allows the first two owners to plant the areas between their woodland edge and fence to enable the three sections to join up and obliterate the enclosure geometry.

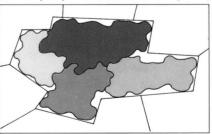

e. The last owner plants his area and the interlocking is completed leading to a unified design.

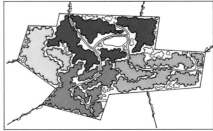

f. The woodland is completely developed as a unit with open space, paths and detailed edge treatment.

The degree of wooded appearance of any area varies, depending on how it is laid out and from where it is seen. Flatter areas may seem heavily wooded due to coalescence of many small woods which actually occupy only a small proportion of the area. As the viewer moves through the landscape, open space, vistas and the change from woodland into built-up areas help to keep the balance right. In other places there may be greater visibility, and as more woodland comes into view there may be a point where there is a sense of over-domination by woodland, and feelings of oppression start to occur. In general a balance of not more than two-thirds visible woodland to one-third open space is a safe proportion, although variety and contrast of woodland extent between particular places should be maintained.

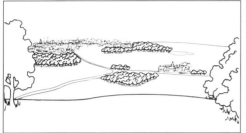

7a. A view from a high point over an area of urban fringe landscape. Rather less than one-third woodland produces an unbalanced composition difficult to unify in a landscape lacking structure.

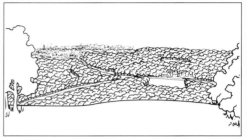

b. Rather more than two-thirds woodland also produces an unbalanced composition when open space is a valued component of the landscape.

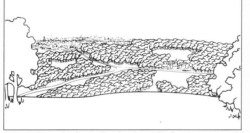

c. Around two-thirds woodland and one-third open space produces a more balanced composition, particularly when the two are interlocked..

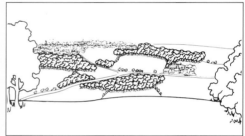

d. One third woodland is also balanced but needs to be tied into other patterns in the landscape in order to achieve unity.

Involving People

Community woodlands will be established in localities where landscape is already in the process of change. New building work and other development on the one hand, gradual erosion in quality of many green belt landscapes on the other, have been features of life on the urban fringe for years. The creation of woodland close to where people live may not always be welcomed. Most areas are likely to see a gradual establishment of woodland. This is easier to accept than sudden large–scale planting. Landscape change will be better managed and controlled where a well designed framework for development has been established at the planning stage, rather than the forest appearing in what seems a haphazard fashion. An associated programme of publicity, information and education will help people to come to terms with this change.

People care about the appearance of woods and forests, and they should be involved so that their wishes are known. It is important to ask people the right questions, to identify those aspects which make up the most preferred landscapes. Recent research carried out for the Forestry Commission and the Countryside Commissions gives an indication of what most people prefer, and how these preferences vary regionally,**"Forests, Woodlands and People's Preferences", Prof T. R. Lee, 1991**. Local surveys could be carried out to check that the main research findings hold good in the locality. The woodland design can then take these preferences into account.

8. People can be involved in community forests in many ways. Here some youngsters are making and erecting nest boxes.

4. DESIGN CONCEPTS

The creation of a new forest or woodland for the community is an exciting but testing task. It requires more than an understanding of physical constraints and possibilities. There must be a vision of what it will look like and how it will be used. Inspiration can come from many sources; from a knowledge of the range of forests and woods found in Britain, from a consideration of what woodlands have to offer as places of escape from the stresses of urban living, from successful examples of similar forests in other countries, and from the possible degree of formality or naturalness which might be used to create variety and drama within the forest.

Design Related to Landscape Character

Britain has a great variety of landscapes and associated forest and woodland, all influenced to a greater or lesser extent by man's activities. They range from wild mountainscapes through remote uplands with extensive new forests, to different intensities of agriculture, with woodlands, hedgerows and parkland, to urban fringe areas, merging into suburbs with street trees, municipal parks and private gardens, and finally to city centres where street trees, endure exhaust fumes and restricted space. The design and layout of woodlands and trees must relate in character to the landscape in which they are situated.

9a. A semi-natural forest where natural forms and features and a feeling of being able to escape from other people is possible.

A strong urban landscape of rectangular forms makes little concession to what little ground shape there is or to soils, watercourses or other natural features. At the other extreme, semi-natural landscapes, are dominated by geology and the form of the ground. Community forests will be the more valued by town and city dwellers as they appear to take on the attributes of the semi-natural as a contrast to their urban surroundings. These are irregular as opposed to regular, diverse rather than ordered, organic or natural instead of the inorganic and geometric of the built environment. Each has a place. The genius of the best examples of community forest in the world is the juxtaposition of the two.

There will usually be an opportunity for a gradation of woodland layout types from a more municipal parkland layout close to the edge of the built environment, moving through a country park type layout, to the more naturalistic appearance of larger woodland areas. Essentially the difference between these is the relative dominance of trees and the formality or informality of their layout. How these layout types interact visually will depend on the avaliability of land on which to create woodland; the proximity of housing and access; the extent to which the design is already compromised by man-made artefacts such as transmission lines, motorways, and large buildings; and the skill and vision of the forest designer.

b. A formal park in complete contrast to a., where order and obvious management create a landscape used by many people every day; the Meadows, Edinburgh.

Sources of Design Ideas

There is no shortage of sources of inspiration and design ideas to help the community forest designer to plan for rich and varied woodland landscapes.

Formal layouts

Formal examples, with dramatic beech or oak avenues, can be found in continental Europe, where there is often a long tradition of good forest and woodland management. These can create stunning visual effects. The woodland between the formal framework can be less rigid. This style can have applications along or near to major roads into cities. The grand avenue can be continued by street trees or can be focused on some features, perhaps a gateway or portal .
A layout dominated by straight avenues has a poor screening capacity; it can be difficult to get away from other people who can be seen down all the avenues.

10. A formal avenue laid out in a former royal hunting forest; Breda, Holland.

Designed parkland

The classical English designed landscapes are examples of a more informal approach. Woodland was carefully sited to form and control vistas, often in association with water and artefacts such as obelisks and follies. These landscapes rely on asymmetrically balanced compositions of mass and open space. The open space is sometimes a relatively minor component.

11. A classical parkland landscape at Gregynog, Powys.

Deer parks and forests

Wilder, much more natural, but still man-made in the strict sense are the relics of old deer forests and parks. These are the result of more or less controlled woodland grazing by a variety of animals over many years. The New Forest is the largest example, with a very rich composition of closed canopy woodland, open woodland, heath, bog, grass pasture and other open spaces. The edges are highly developed ecologically and visually, contributing much to the landscape character. Sutton Park, near Birmingham, is a smaller example within an urban setting. Woodlands of this type have a high value for wildlife and high recreational potential.

12. A path leading into woodland at Sutton Park giving an immediate sense of wildness and escape from the nearby town.

European town forests

Many European towns have forests on the urban fringe. Some have been owned and managed by the municipality for centuries, often with the original object of securing fuel supplies; others are former royal or aristocratic properties, established as hunting and amenity woodlands, which later passed into public ownership. An increasing number are of comparatively recent origin, deliberately created to enhance the local environment and recreational facilities. The most successful of these town forests combine more formal areas with other areas set aside to be quite wild. The essential feature is the size and shape of the site. The best are large enough to accommodate a wide range of uses by spatial separation.

13. The Mastbos at Breda, Holland. A long established forest on the edge of the town heavily used for recreation.

14. The Riskov, Aarhus, Denmark. This forest within the city, has been used by the inhabitants for several centuries. It is characterised by many mature beech and oak trees forming the canopy.

15.The Amsterdamse Bos, Holland. This designed forest, planted in the 1930s provides a major recreational resource. The many water areas together with open space and mass of woodland create a superb landscape.

16. The city of Stuttgart, Germany is enveloped by woodlands on its south and west sides. The trees continue into and among the houses providing stronger links between city and forest.

Woodland form and structure

There is scope for ideas and imaginative variety in the diversity of possible woodland structures and composition; these are more important in many ways than the precise selection of species. Design can create woodland appropriate to its particular uses at the outset, without requiring it to pass through an obvious "plantation" stage.

Whatever sources of ideas and inspiration are used to arrive at a satisfactory design concept, the use of conifers, broadleaves and mixtures of the two offers possibilities. The evergreen conifers are valuable for maintaining screening, shelter and colour in the months when the broadleaves are leafless. Large well-shaped conifers can be dramatic. The variety of shapes, textures and colours are a valuable source of diversity. Large spreading broadleaves will eventually produce a strong spirit of place and a feeling of age and continuity with earlier times but there is an intimidating length of time to go through before they contribute in this way. The designer can use their wide range of forms, seasonal leaf colour and bark colour with good effect.

17. Westonbirt Arboretum, Gloucestershire, where the autumn colours show off the features of a wide range of broadleaved trees.

18. Bedgebury Pinetum, Kent, where the form and colours of different conifers are displayed in a designed setting.

Open space is a vital element. In the New Forest the open spaces are at least as valuable to the structure and pattern as the areas of closed canopy woodland. Within a given area of community woodland, as a rule of thumb, open space of around one-third of the total would be reasonable. Recreational activities often need open space where sunlight reaches the ground and air circulation keeps the surface sufficiently dry. Space can be kept open by management or allowed to 'migrate' as it will eventually under coppicing or other regimes. Each type of open space has its own design requirements. The design concept must embody a clear decision on the desirable extent and forms of open space.

How should each of these potential types and characters of woodland and open space be arranged? The design concept has to answer this question and suggest the patterns likely to meet the various community forest objectives. For example, it might propose a gradation, with relatively formal layout within and close to the urban edge, becoming less formal with increasing distance from the built-up areas. This pattern could transform into an interlocking arrangement with the farmed landscapes beyond, where small woods among fields predominate. The gradual change from tame to wild could be used to spread recreational loads and to provide reassurance to people unused to forest surroundings.

The chosen arrangements need not be uniform over the whole area. 'Fingers' of wilder woodland could be established into the urban edge to provide connections and corridors to town parkland and green space, possibly along access routes. Another possibility is to have a dramatic contrast between townscape and woodland, rather than a gradation. This is consistent with the idea of the woodland as another world, emphasised by the design of 'gateways' - either man-made features or particularly definitive woodland - through which one passes from city to forest.

19. An open space set among the mature beech trees of the New Forest. Maintained by grazing animals these spaces are as much a part of the forest as the trees themselves.

20. A large open space ringed by woodlands at Sutton Park. The edge transition from trees to open ground and the screening of the urban areas from view add to the character of the space and its scale.

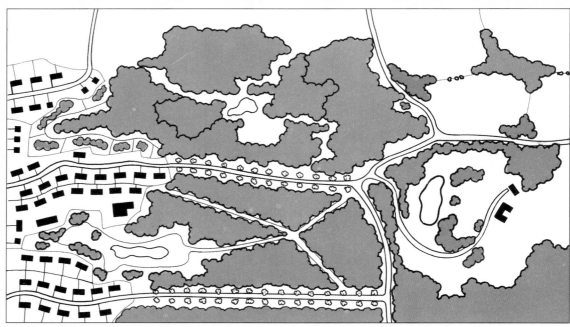

21. A diagrammatic layout of woodland areas on the urban fringe showing the changes in woodland type and extent possible, from the very formal through the naturalistic to an enclosed agricultural landscape.

5. VISUAL DESIGN PRINCIPLES

The aesthetics of woodland design require an understanding of landscape design principles. The principles described below have been tried and tested in a wide variety of landscape types. They are used to analyse the components of the existing landscape and so identify its character, and to compose the constituent parts of the forest into a unified and satisfying design. They are also helpful in explaining or presenting a design, especially to non-designers.

Shape

Shape is a dominant factor of design, with a powerful and evocative effect on how we see our surroundings. Particularly important is the distinction between geometric and organic or natural shapes, which has a profound influence on our perception of woodland as man-made or natural. Correct choice and design of shapes in woodland layout is vital.

Perception of a shape is influenced by its overall proportions, viewing direction, and the nature of the external boundary edge, whether sharply defined or diffuse. The proportions of all landscapes are broadly horizontal, so diagonal shapes on a slope tend to look more relaxed; lines at right angles to the contour are rarely pleasing.

22a. Basic geometric shapes.
b. Natural shapes.

23. A geometric woodland shape superimposed among more natural shapes of landform and vegetation.

Visual Force

Static objects or images often appear to move or exert influence over the way we look at the landscape. The eye and mind respond to these visual forces in a predictable and dynamic way. Looking at landform, we find our eyes drawn down convex slopes and up concave ones, the strength of the visual force depending on the scale and irregularity of the landform.

Where landform, even of low relief, is noticeable, woodland should be designed to follow visual forces by rising up in hollows and falling on spurs and ridges. This helps to avoid visual conflict between shapes and creates a well-unified relationship between the woodland and landform. The pattern of natural vegetation is often similar, with plants from lower ground extending higher in sheltered hollows than on exposed ridges.

24. This black and white pattern induces a sensation of twisting movement.

25. This sinuous line seems to be wriggling or meandering in a serpentine fashion.

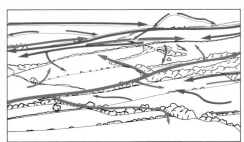

26a. An area of landscape in the Mendip Hills.

b. The visual force analysis. The stronger arrows identify more important features in the landform.

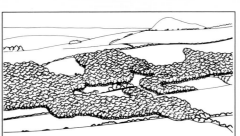

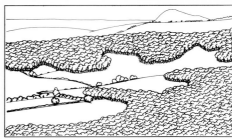

c. Planting in the valley flows up into the hollows following upward forces with the open ground retained on the ridges and convexities following downward forces.

d. Planting on the ridges and knolls is the reverse of c. but responds to landform in the same way.

Scale

Scale is a matter of relative and absolute size, and has a major effect on perception. The scale of a forest or woodland should reflect the scale of the landscape. Much depends on the location of the viewpoint. The scale of the landscape increases the further you can see, the wider the unrestricted view, and the higher the elevation of the observer. The scale of the landscape is thus larger on higher slopes and hilltops than on lower slopes and valleys. Areas appear to be of different size when seen from different points. Small shapes may appear to be out of scale when viewed from a distance in a large scale landscape. The designer frequently has to resolve scale both from short views within the woodland and more distant views from outside.

It follows that as the scale of the landscape changes, so should the scale of the woodland shapes, with gradual change from one area to another. When a landscape is seen as being divided into distinct parts, a ratio of one-third to two-thirds is often the most satisfying. A hillside which appears to be one-third open and two-thirds wooded, or *vice versa* looks pleasing, whereas a proportion of half and half produces a feeling of unnatural symmetry.

The woodland landscape designer can use the techniques of *closure*, *nearness* and *coalescence* to organise smaller elements in the landscape to create a larger scale pattern or arrangement. The use of *interlock*, described below, is also an effective device for achieving the desirable scale of design.

When an element appears to enclose a space, the element and the space seem to become one. Closure can be used to increase the apparent scale of small woodlands to reflect the scale of the landscape. Too much closure can have the effect of separating sections of the landscape, and this can reduce unity. As well as its effect on scale, closure is useful for giving structure to a landscape where it is otherwise lacking.

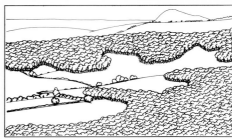

27. Seen from a hilltop this is a large scale landscape. Penshaw Monument, Tyne and Wear.

28. Inside a woodland glade scale is contained by a combination of distance across the space and the height of the trees. Wendover Woods, Bucks.

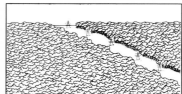

29a. Seen close to the spaces alongside this powerline appear quite varied.

b. Seen from a distance, however, the major effect is still strongly linear and the shaped edges are relatively insignificant.

When elements are positioned far apart they tend to be seen as completely separate, but when placed close together they are seen as a group. Nearness is another useful device to increase the apparent scale of small woods or clumps of trees and to give some structure and balance to a landscape.

By positioning small woods and trees in such a way that they coalesce, overlapping each other when seen from certain viewpoints, an impression of a more heavily wooded landscape can result which may be more appropriate in scale. This effect causes some parts of the country, Sussex and Surrey for example, to appear more wooded than they really are. This technique is specially useful in design in more horizontal landscapes, where distances between elements are foreshortened.

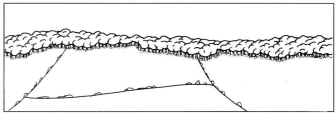

30a. *Woodland occupying less than one third of the composition looks too small and unbalanced.*

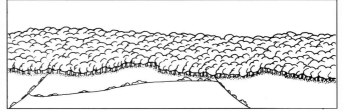

b. *Fifty per cent woodland also looks unbalanced because neither element is dominant.*

c. *One-third woodland produces a far more satisfactory result.*

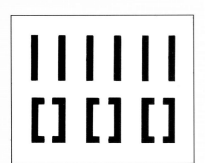

31a. *In this abstract example the six black bars are merely arranged in a row.*
b. *By turning the ends inwards three distinct enclosed spaces are created and the shapes becomes unified.*

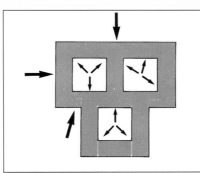

32a. *Complete closure creates inward looking spaces and connections are lost with the area outside.*

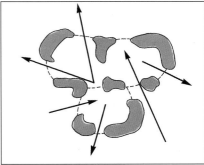

b. *Partial closure retains the sense of space but allows it to flow into and out of the enclosed area providing more continuity in the design.*

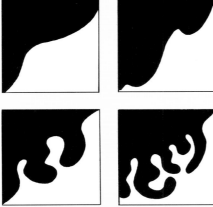

33. *In each succeeding diagram there is increasing interlock of the black and white shapes .*

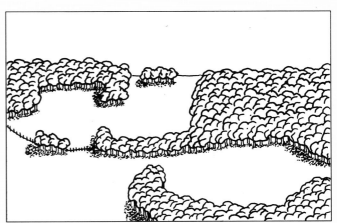

34. *The open space and the woodland areas interlock together, create closure and so produce a more resolved scale of individual elements as well as a more unified design.*

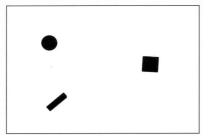

35a. Three shapes positioned separately.

b. When near each other they are seen as a group.

36a. Three small woods or clumps of trees in an open landscape.

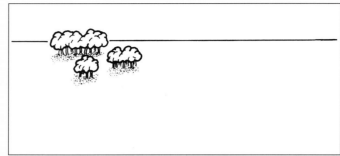

b. If planted closer together they tend to read as a group and assume a larger scale.

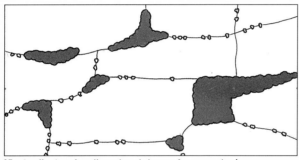

37a. A collection of small woods and clumps of trees seen in plan.

b. When seen in the view the woods appear to coalesce together and the landscape appears more wooded than it really is.

38. Belts and groups of trees coalesce to produce a well wooded effect in this parkland near Jedburgh, Borders.

Diversity

This is the number and degree of different features in a landscape or design. It is a treasured feature of the British landscape as a result of varied geology, climate and the long history of human settlement and land use. Landscape diversity is linked to ecological diversity, but the two are distinct and not necessarily equivalent.

Woods and forests introduce visual diversity into treeless landscapes, but newly created young woodland, whether broadleaved or conifer, can reduce diversity if it hides landscape detail. We should take the opportunity to create diversity in otherwise uniform landscapes, but not overdo it. Excessive diversity often leads to restless confusion in a landscape design.

Increased diversity can have the effect of reducing scale and may be so used where this is desirable. A high level of diversity is acceptable if one element is clearly dominant. For example, one species might occupy two-thirds of a wood with the remaining third consisting of a variety of species. In many cases diversity has to be incorporated at different scales, depending on the extent to which a wood is seen from external or internal viewpoints.

39. A typical scene in the English lowlands where the field pattern, crop and soil colours, trees and woods, nucleated settlements and individual farmsteads produce a rich, diverse landscape.

40. An urban fringe landscape where too much apparently random diversity leads to confusion and a breakdown of landscape structure. Canford Heath.

Unity

This is an essential aim of landscape design and can be achieved in a number of ways. The use of compatible or similar shapes, visual force and scale will unite the woodland with the landscape and counterbalance contrasts of colour, texture and form.

Much of the coherence of various patterns in the landscape is due to the interlocking of shapes. This seems to give one shape a stronger visual connection with another. Interlock can be at a large scale, as in the broad pattern of open space and woodland, or at a very small scale, for example between two species in a woodland. A high degree of interlock gives more unity to a design.

Even-aged woodland tends to be highly unified and lacking in diversity. It often contrasts strongly with open ground beyond it, through darker colour, stronger shadows, coarser texture and the height of the trees. These contrasts are softened by designing shapes, external margins, open space within the woodland, and the pattern of species and woodland structure, so that shapes interlock and unite the forest with the surrounding landscape.

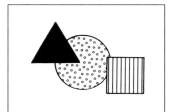

41a Three different forms which, though spatially connected, are not creating a unified composition.

b. Similarity of shape and orientation helps to unify this composition.

42. The interlocking of woodland and open ground helps create a unified design where scale is resolved and the shapes are compatible.

"The Spirit of the Place"

When these design principles are satisfied there will remain something unique to a particular place; this is an important asset and stimulus to good design which should be conserved and if possible enhanced. It is often expressed by particular contrasts or combinations of features. Forest design should ensure that these features are emphasised, not hidden. Enclosed valleys, or very exposed summits or high points; indications of great antiquity, such as old trees and rocks; places where the lighting is dramatic, especially where associated with water; all these contribute to a powerful sense of place, particularly where there is a feeling of wilderness.

This aspect of landscape design is elusive, and easier to conserve where it already exists than to create. The features and qualities which contribute to it should be recognised and incorporated in the designs for individual sites. Spirit of place is often associated with small areas but it may be a major contributor to landscape character; hence the importance of the initial landscape appraisal in recognising, understanding and applying it.

It may be difficult to identify a strong sense of place in areas intended to develop as community woodlands, but look for particular historical connections, aspects of heritage, nuclei of areas such as old parkland or designed landscapes, or associations with pre-industrial or early industrial times Any of these can provide a basis for creating a spirit of place even where it does not exist strongly. This is a challenge for the community forest designer.

43. This gnarled old tree, full of character helps to impart a sense of place to Sherwood Forest, perhaps the more powerful since its age links us with the past.

44. Man-made features such as this piece of sculpture at Grizedale Forest can help create a sense of place, in a new woodland lacking old trees or other long established features.

6. THE LAYOUT OF WOODLANDS

The layout of individual woods needs to take account of the overall landscape character of the area as well as accommodating the detailed design objectives, such as providing shelter, screening and so on. For the design of larger woodlands, experience has shown that a logical approach is to:

- design the shape of the external margins and establish the scale of the woodland in the landscape;
- design the areas of various woodland types to create interlocking shapes in scale with the rest of the woodland;
- design the layout of the open spaces.

The shape and scale of the external margins are the first consideration. Wherever an informal or natural layout has been chosen and landform dominates, shape should respond, with margins rising in hollows and falling on convexities. The importance of even quite subtle landforms should not be underestimated. Care is necessary if a relatively formal layout is chosen for an area of strong landform. Formal effects work best as arrangements of mass and space within woodland rather than geometric external shapes.

The scale of the woodland units must relate to the scale of the landscape. This includes the relationship of the heights of the trees to the spaces between woods and other features. You may have to draw sections or sketches to display the eventual heights of trees and so evaluate the scale effects.

It may be necessary to leave some ground unplanted to achieve the best shape and scale, and to aid the interlock of woodland and open space at the edge. The management of the unplanted areas may have to be arranged, particulary if they adjoin arable land.

The size of woodlands has a marked effect on the degree and intensity of possible recreational uses, and on the amount of open space they can accommodate.

Size of woodland and recreational potential

>75 ha   Woodland capable of handling large numbers of people. Open spaces and sense of seclusion possible with over 100 000 visitors per year. Woods over 300 ha are capable of absorbing huge numbers of visitors.

50-75 ha   Lower size range for significant level of use. Open space and secluded wild areas possible. Variety of woodland structure and quite a wide range of recreation types available.

25-50 ha   Good path network possible and some open space, but visual carrying capacity lower due to intervisibility of paths. More difficult to feel alone. A range of informal recreational possible, but not noisy types.

10 -25 ha   Informal recreation possible, mainly with small open spaces. Disturbance to wildlife likely to be much greater and intensive use may make it feel crowded.

1-10 ha   Low visual carrying capacity; small number of uses per wood. Wildlife very disturbed. Wear and tear high.

<1 ha   Very limited recreation use, mainly limited to paths through woods. Some informal play. Valuable as landscape elements.

Particular sizes of woodland areas and open space may be required for specific wildlife conservation requirements, such as the need to maintain the correct level of light beneath the tree canopy, or allowing adequate sunlight to reach the floor of open spaces.

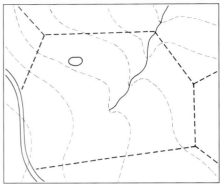

45a. A piece of land chosen to be planted as part of a community woodland.

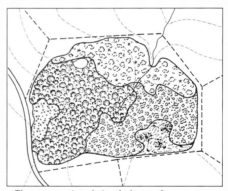

b. The external margin is designed. Here account is taken of the landform, the stream and the public roadside.

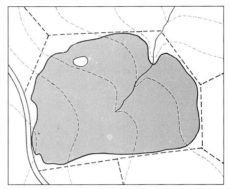

c. The next stage is to design the layout of different woodland types.

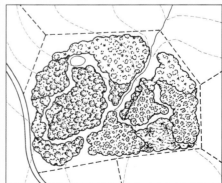

d. Finally the open spaces are designed into the woodland - the stream, a pond and footpath routes. Some of these coincide with the edges between the woodland types.

A drawback of a formal, regular layout is the stiffness and artificial feeling of stands of different ages and species and of open space. Such a layout does not lend itself to natural edges. The latter are easier to obtain where different areas within the wood are of irregular shape, interlocking with each other and so maximising the total length of edge. The visual and ecological importance of edges is outlined in section 8.

Layout of open spaces within woodland is a key part of design and is described in detail in section 8. A single open space usually serves several purposes; for example, wildlife habitat, walking routes, vistas and access for maintenance. There is, therefore, a marked long-term benefit in designing the permanent open spaces to form a system, with corridors or pathways linking larger spaces and all with fully developed edges. The open spaces will retain the sense of permanence, stability and familiarity when woodland management requires some trees to be felled and replaced from time to time.

In this way the dynamic nature of the woodland can be maintained within a long-term framework or structure. Research studies tell us that many visitors to forests are easily disoriented and require reassurance. Physical structures such as waymarking, and mapboards help in this; so does the use of subtle reassurance in the form of landmarks, perhaps glimpses of a folly or feature on a high point, and recognisable open spaces through which the visitor travels and gains ' locational reassurance'.

Maintaining the correct scale may be difficult in the design of small woods. An existing strong pattern of hedgerows and trees can allow them to be shaped and fitted into a satisfactory composition, or it may be necessary to create a pattern using interlock, coalescence and overlap. Where a hedgerow pattern is weak or absent, landform must guide design in all but the flattest landscapes.

Game coverts are a feature on many farms and may exist on the fringes of urban areas. Their design is complicated by the need to combine their sporting functions within an acceptable landscape arrangement. Open space within the small coverts and the pattern of woodland types is less important than the overall layout. **"Lowland Landscape Design Guidelines" (Forestry Commission, 1991) gives detailed advice on the design of small woods and game coverts in predominantly agricultural landscapes.**

46. A relatively formal section of the Amsterdamse Bos where a sweeping open space is defined by simple, bold masses of woodland on either side.

47. A very small wood in a new town, surrounded by housing and under a lot of pressure from litter and children playing.

48. A generously scaled open space provides a view over water towards the woodland edge. The curving path leads the walker out into and across the space. Amsterdamse Bos.

7. WOODLAND STRUCTURE

A new woodland needs time to develop a structure of trees, shrubs and ground vegetation and this process is continuously influenced by the silvicultural management of the trees. It is important at the planning stage to consider what woodland structure and management regime is best suited in different areas to meet the objectives of the planting. This has an influence on species choice, the spacing and arrangement of trees and on the distribution of open space. Visually and ecologically, and for many recreational purposes, the woodland structure is more important than the diversity of tree species it contains. A vision of the eventual woodland structure helps to identify the potential of new planting, as well as being applicable to existing woodlands.

Much of the internal diversity of a woodland is provided by the various stand structures, with different structural types often contrasting quite strongly with each other. The aesthetic qualities of certain types can be very high; bluebells carpeting the clear floor of an oak wood in spring; the soaring trunks of pines reaching high overhead with shafts of sunlight penetrating to heathery ground layer; the effect of light and dapple shade along a footpath; the space enclosed by the spreading crowns of mature beech tree, with the dry rustle of dead leaves under foot. By identifying the possible place in the design for particular structures which could be developed, the landscape designer can provide for a diverse series of visual experiences for users to enjoy as they move through the woodlands.

49. A carpet of bluebells beneath the fresh green beech canopy.

50. The majestic soaring trunks of a stand of Douglas fir.

51. The rich structure of an ancient woodland.

52. Autumn leaves form a dry rustling layer underfoot.

Silvicultural Systems and their Applications

Systems of woodland management fall into three categories; *High forest* is the term applied to those woods where the trees are of seedling origin; the trees in *Coppice* woods arise from the shoots which sprout from the stumps of recently felled trees. *Coppice-with-standards* is a combination of the other two.

High forest is the predominant form of woodland. All natural woodlands are high forest. There are many variants, depending on whether the forest contains one or more species and how intimately they are mixed, and the extent to which more than one age or size class occurs. The stocking in these woods can be managed to control the crown development, and therefore the stem diameters, of individual trees, also the amount of light reaching understorey trees, shrub or herb layers.

The simpler forms of high forest consist of more or less even aged stands which are felled and restocked, either by planting or natural seeding from nearby mother trees. A wood or forest consisting of even aged stands of varying ages can provide a good deal of variety and interest, particularly if there is diversity of tree species and a good alternation of young, middle aged and old stands, and where adjoining space extends beneath the canopy. This structure is likely to be the simplest to achieve in community woods, at least during the first generation of trees.

The woodland is more diverse visually where the structure is more complex. There is a greater wealth of detail to see, and such woods tend to appear wilder and more natural. Woods with several canopy layers, or managed by small- scale fellings to give groups of young and middle-aged trees alongside mature trees, have a high degree of interest. Light comes through the branches and understorey layers in varying intensities, fellings are unobtrusive and there is a greater sense of continuity and permanence. This is often a preferable state but is a long way off in most community forests except where there are existing woodlands.

The understorey is particularly important where a high visual carrying capacity is required. Dense shrubs or young trees growing above head height prevent people seeing each other across the woodland. This increases the number of people a wood can contain without it feeling crowded. Understoreys of hazel, beech or hornbeam are effective, while holly provides evergreen screening and spatial composition all year round. Disturbance to wildlife can be lessened when undergrowth provides safe cover for animals and helps to prevent people and dogs from straying too far from paths. Bramble is excellent for this purpose.

The visual effects of shape and scale have to be resolved both in the layout of woodland types and in relation to the felling and regeneration regime later on, especially if the woodland is on a hillside or can be seen from a vantage point outside. Small felling 'coupes' (the individual areas of felling) sometimes appear moth-eaten. Clear felled coupes of bigger scale may be preferable. Such coupes on skylines can open up views out of the woodland which may be valuable. **"The Lowland Landscape Design Guidelines"** give detailed advice on the visual aspects of various options for felling and regeneration.

53. A beech high forest where openings have been made in the fore and middleground for regeneration to take place. Otherwise it is devoid of understorey and it is possible to see right through the stand. Aarhus, Denmark.

54. A mixed storey formed by regenerating beech in the Chilterns. Views beneath the canopy are blocked and the scale reduced.

55. Dense brambles on either side of this path through woodland prevent undue disturbance to wildlife. Stevenage, Herts.

Coppice woods are always the result of human management. In former times this type of woodland was widespread because the system produced the fuel and timber which people then required. Areas of coppice were managed on a rotational basis, felling so much annually or every few years, when the coppice stems had reached the desired size; age of the stems at felling was generally 20 to 40 years, depending on the species and site productivity.

With the relatively short cycle of felling in adjacent areas and a range of different ages and heights, coppice woodland can have a very diverse spatial structure. The ground surface vegetation is exposed to full light more frequently than under high forest, and this may bring benefits to wildlife. Being deciduous, coppice woods can be dull and gloomy in winter, but in spring the field layer of flowering plants can be very rich. Again, shape and scale of coupes becomes important if the woodland is visible externally. This system could be established within twenty years of planting if the right species are chosen.

Coppice-with-standards was also once widespread. The system combines simple coppice of even age, grown as the underwood, and standards of uneven age treated under the high forest selection system as the overwood. Standards are seedling trees, or well-shaped coppice stems retained when the coppice is cut, grown on rotations equal to several coppice rotations. This provides larger dimensions of timber than can be obtained from the coppice. The retention of standards over several coppice rotations makes for a greater degree of visual continuity than in simple coppice.

Wood pasture and wooded parkland are combinations of high forest and pastoral agriculture which also had a place in earlier times. They provided both grazing and timber for local needs within an open structure, in which open grown trees developed large crowns and great character. These are quite easy to manage and could well find their place in the range of woodland types in a community forest.

Eventually there may be areas where the maintenance of continous woodland cover is a high priority. This can be done by small-scale regeneration fellings, or by underplanting older stands to create understoreys to be retained for visual cover when the old trees are eventually cut. It should be appreciated that these approaches require a high intensity of management, often over a long period, and it is best to limit them to those areas where they are specially desirable. It is impractical and unwise to propose detailed and intricate management over extensive areas of community forest. The landscape design requirements can nearly always be met by simpler methods.

56. Harvesting in chestnut coppice. Kent.

57. Coppice with standards provide a high level of stand diversity and rich wildlife habitat. Bradfield Woods, Suffolk.

58. Pigs foraging for acorns (pannage), New Forest.

Establishing a Woodland Atmosphere Quickly

Some time must elapse between planting a wood and being able to use it fully for recreation, though there is some educational value in seeing a young wood develop, especially to those who helped to plant it. This time can be shortened by using a proportion of fast growing pioneer species both broadleaves and conifers, which can get above head height in four to five years.

A feeling of woodland can thus be achieved quickly, allowing some low intensity recreational use. These pioneer species may be silviculturally beneficial on many sites, either as nurse species or to create better conditions for establishing the long-term species later. Shrubs can be interspersed in the first few rows of trees on the woodland edges. Hedge plants can also be established at time of planting, perhaps as an eventual replacement for fences.

The long term effects of tree growth are best taken into consideration at the time of planting. Though it is possible to plant an area, see how it develops, then cut paths and openings in it, the pattern of woodland types, open spaces, internal edges and outside margins, and the eventual felling and regeneration is better when planned from the start. Plans may need to allow for the progressive widening of access routes to maintain optimum conditions of light and air circulation. Thinning to allow undergrowth to flourish also needs careful planning and timing. The planning of wildlife conservation management should also be done early. Any areas intended to be set aside without further treatment to develop into 'wild' corners should be similarly identified.

It is especially important to lay down the access route system when the terrain is easy to see, preferably at the survey stage. Paths and road alignments should be identified, with sufficient alternatives so that general access and recreational use can continue when harvesting or other potentially hazardous operations require part of the road system to be closed. Alternative paths are also necessary to allow closure of over-used routes for recovery and repair. The landscape design requirements of roads and paths should be defined at the early planning stage so that they can be incorporated when planting is done.

59. Dense, fast growing birch has created a woodland effect very quickly in this urban fringe setting.

8. DESIGN OF OPEN SPACE

Planning the Open Space System

The first step is to identify the valuable open spaces which already exist in the area. This should form part of the appraisal survey. Existing open spaces may be streams, ponds, wet areas, meadows and other open habitats, archaeological and historical sites, public roads, footpaths, railways, buildings and service corridors such as transmission lines.

The designer must then consider the open space requirements of the forest in terms of landscape design, to provide visual diversity, interlock of shapes, as recreational open space, for wildlife conservation, for access and service needs, and so on. To what extent do existing open spaces meet these requirements? Should some be extended or new ones formed? Which existing open spaces serve no particular purpose and should be planted?

Once the open spaces required by the woodland design have been identified, links can be made and the whole system developed as part of the long term structure. The location of some open spaces, for recreation for example, will not always be known from the start. As long as the main structure is defined, it is not difficult to incorporate additional elements later. The shape, size and scale of open spaces will depend on whether they are based on precise dimensions, such as minimum widths of clearance for transmission lines or the size of a games pitch, or whether, like streamside or roadside space, they may be varied to create diversity.

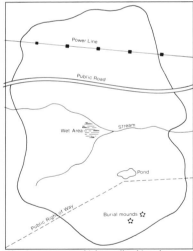

60a. An area upon which woodland is to be created but criss-crossed with features requiring to be kept open.

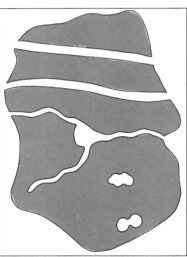

b. If minimal requirements were met a series of unconnected and basic gaps would be left in the planting.

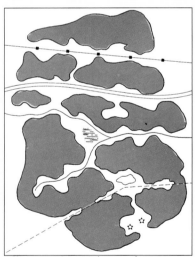

c. Here a more integrated system of open spaces has been created, with linking sections, views and wildlife corridors built in.

Woodland Edges

In design terms margins and edges are different. Margins define the shape of a space; the edge is a matter of individual elements of single trees and small groups. The edge detail is usually superimposed on a previously designed margin. The requirements of external edges may be the most obvious, but the same detailed treatments should be applied within the woodland, wherever trees adjoin more or less open ground. The shape of the forest margin must be attractive, and completely designed before details of edge treatment are worked out. Edges, no matter how well designed, will not improve bad shapes.

Where there is no existing pattern of trees in the surrounding landscape, the edge should reflect landform or the pattern of ground vegetation. There are useful pointers in the gradual changes to be seen in the transition from woodland to open ground in the natural forest.

In man-made woodlands edges can be made to look more natural and in scale with the landscape by:

Detailing shaping of the edge. Protrusions and indentations of the main mass of the woodland are important visual links.They should follow landform in the same way as woodland shapes. They should be irregular in size and distribution to avoid unnatural symmetry.

-Using species with different growth rates to vary tree height on the edge. This avoids a continuous wall effect, particularly with conifers. Create tapered edges by transitions from fast-growing trees, through slower trees to shrub species. This should be done in appropriate places, along roadsides for example, or where edges cross prominent skylines or ridges.

Increasing tree spacing towards the edge of the wood. Wider spacing should be irregular, particularly in small-scale landscapes, or close to roads and paths. Regular spacing looks artificial. Treatment must be bold if it is not to be visually insignificant.

-Establishing irregular outlying groups. These should be near enough to the woodland to be seen as part of it, not 'free-floating', and positioned so as to seem to be a natural extension. Avoid too many groups, which make the scale too small and may themselves appear artificial..

-Planting individual trees close to the forest edge or outlying groups, to link the woodland with open ground. Give them room to develop well-shaped crowns.

The opportunity to establish ecologically and visually diverse edges at time of planting should not be missed. It is cheaper to do it then and the results will be better. The designer should have a clear understanding of the wildlife value of edges. An 'ecological edge' occurs at the boundary of two habitats or plant communities. Watercourses illustrate this, with a sequence of zones where aquatic vegetation gives way to bankside grasses and herbs, then to taller grass and small shrubs, then perhaps to larger shrubs and trees. Ecological edges also have a vertical component, with edges occuring between the different levels of shrub layers and tree crowns.

The ecological value of an edge is almost always greater than the value of the interior of individual habitats adjoining, because of the range of plant life in a relatively small space, and the needs of some species to use the neighbouring habitats, perhaps feeding in one and finding cover in another. Good landscape design can contribute to this through diversity of ground vegetation, shrub, understorey and canopy layers in various combinations. The variation in light and moisture provided by different ages, species and densities of trees in an irregular edge greatly increases the wildlife value of woodland, and makes it look much more interesting

61. A graded, well structured edge which has been partly created by grazing and browsing animals. Sutton Park, W Midlands.

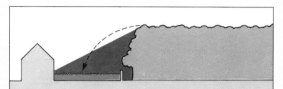

62a. Woodland edges near housing need careful design to avoid shading, damage from falling trees and feelings of oppression from the dark woodland.

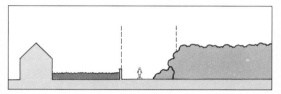

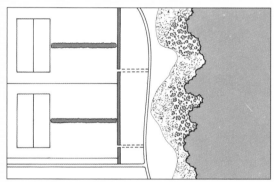

b and c. An edge zone, (in section and plan) perhaps with a path along it, where the graded structure can develop helps solves these problems .

63. A woodland edge set back from housing. The strip in between is mown with and contains an access footpath. Stevenage, Herts.

Streamsides

Streams must have adequate width (at least 5 m) of thriving bankside vegetation to minimse erosion and protect water quality. The aim should be to have an irregular distribution of streamside broadleaved trees with about 50% of the stream in full sunlight, the rest in dappled shade (Forestry Commission 1988). This type of bankside is suitable for fishing, with open areas for casting. Access to the streamside is necessary for inspection and maintenance work, including in some circumstances the removal of dumped rubbish .

Where streams emerge from the lower margin of the woodland in steeper country, the streamside space should be widened in asymmetrical bell-mouth fashion. This is particularly important where streams meet lake shores.

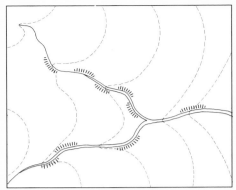

65a. A stream in an area ready to be planted.

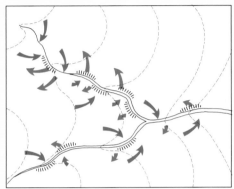

b. An analysis of the detailed landform adjacent to the stream.

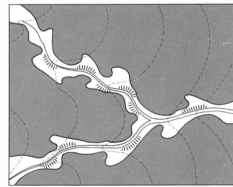

c. The basic woodland canopy edge designed to follow the landform.

64. A stream with well developed bankside vegetation being managed to maximise water quality, aquatic life and the wildlife value of the corridor.

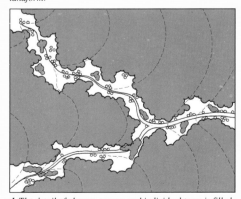

d. The detail of clumps, groups and individual trees is filled in to create the dapple shade requirements.

Open Water

Any body of water is a great attraction to visitors and a highly valued component of the landscape. Woodland design around lakes and reservoirs is particularly sensitive because of the quality of the flat reflective water surface. Continous woodland around a lake tends to divide the lighter sky and water by a dark band. Open ground, with its intermediate colour and texture, can unite the landscape. The ideal is an interlocking pattern of forest and open ground. Some promontories are best kept treeless so that there are views across to water beyond. Trees should be brought to the water's edge at some points, otherwise the forest will seem to float on a ribbon of open space. Groups of trees which overlap with the forest edge and which overhang the water act as necessary links between water and woodland.

Steams and lakesides are important as wildlife habitats and the needs of the latter must be balanced with those of landscape. The ideal is to establish a broad pattern of woodland edges, with dense tree cover merging into low scrub, then open space - which may well be wetland or waterside vegetation - so giving a gradual change of vertical scale. Where lakes are used for water-based recreation such as sailing, the amount of woodland and its distance from the lake may need to be modified significantly to maintain wind flow over the lake surface. This will vary according to topography and the size of the lake.

Woodland design around marshes and bogs should observe the same principles. As time goes on, the edge vegetation may require some management to prevent woodland species colonising the fringes of the wetland.

66. A small lake showing varied structure and open space around its edges. Alice Holt, Surrey.

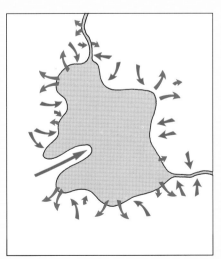

67a. A lake falling within a new woodland area, analysed in terms of landform around its margin.

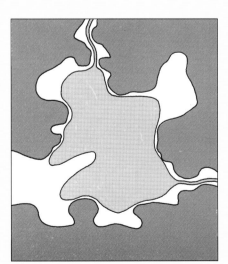

b. The basic woodland canopy edge is designed. A balance between woodland mass, open unwooded space and the water plane should be sought.

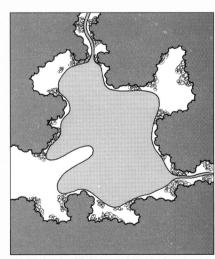

c. Edge detail is filled in once the basic shape is established.

Roadsides

Driving through a corridor of undifferentiated forest for any length of time becomes monotonous. A sequence of views and a succession of varied spaces is required to make the experience interesting. Motorists cannot take in a wealth of detail. Public road margins must be designed on a broad scale and related to the average speed of traffic.

For reasons of safety landscape must be simple and undistracting at junctions, sharp bends, steep hills and blind summits. The attention of the driver must be on the road and visibility requirements of the highway authorities must be met. Forest roads leading off the public road should be carefully planned to avoid them being used as short cuts or fast sections. It may be necessary to introduce bends on the forest road to slow down traffic, particularly at junctions, and to avoid conflict with recreational use.

The woodland margin can usefully be brought closer to the road on bends and steep hills, where the constricted space increases the sense of movement, and kept further back on gentle alignments, with occasional features near the road. The effect should be that of a rhythmic space flowing from one side of the road to the other, with views appearing at intervals. Views opened deliberately through the woodland from public roads must be splayed out at acute angles, otherwise car occupants will miss them altogether.

Where the road passes through an area where small woods come close to the road, these are best staggered on either side. Parallel belts should be avoided.

68. A varied roadside edge with some open space running beneath the canopy, sunlight and shade and a strong group of trees on the left hand side.

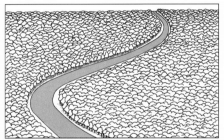

69a A curving road passing through a woodland with a boring parallel edge.

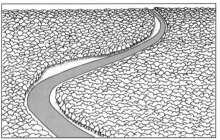

b. A degree of variation is introduced on the outside of bends but the space is still uninteresting.

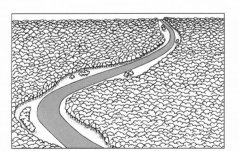

c. Rather more spatial variation together with some punctuating detail is introduced.

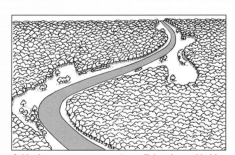

d. Much more generous openings off the edge and bolder groups give a strong sense of rhythm.

e. The edge has become rather too fragmented and scale is too small.

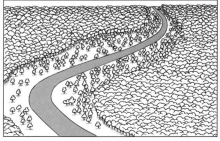

f. Too much variation at too small a scale creates a boring diffuse edge similar to (a.).

Footpaths

Footpaths and other access routes are the principal means from which people experience the forest; the sequential characters, structures, spaces and views are therefore key elements of the design. To make the most of the views, routes should relate to landform. A hierarchy of routes defined by their degree of surfacing and finish should be considered. These should start with routes where people cannot get lost but may include others which convey a sense of exploration.

Footpath routes are the most flexible elements in the open space system. Their design provides great scope for the imagination. They should not be in the open all the time, as walking beneath the tree canopy is often pleasant, but sunshine is such a valuable asset in Britain that paths should pass through open spaces for much of the time.

The space occupied by a path should be diverse in the same way as roadside design The width of the space must vary depending on tree size and topography to avoid it being too open or too oppresive. Where the path runs along the edge of a large open space it is a good idea to keep it partly in and partly out of the woodland, with edge trees and shrubs between the path and the space. This helps to keep the open space seeming wild and empty, if so desired, and provides some shelter and a variety of views along the path.

Some routes will be simple circular walks back to a car park or access point; others will lead walkers to features of particular interest, such as viewpoints, old trees, archaeological sites or ecologically rich area. Passage over waterbodies is always an asset.A survey of such features should be made when planning footpaths and the route then designed to link them. Viewpoints are particularly important as they help to orient the walker within the wood.

Walking, cycling and horse riding routes can be laid out, separated from each other but roughly parallel. This minimises conflicts between users.Particular design skill and imagination is needed where such routes converge at junctions and stream crossings.

If possible the path network should provide alternative routes to give variety. Where a sizeable wood is close to houses it may be desirable to have a perimeter path along the edge, or just inside, with plenty of access points. This will reduce 'unofficial' access and damage to fences or hedges, and allows the woodland path to be used as part of the local pedestrian circulation. The design of well used paths through woodland near housing, or between houses and bus stops, shops and main roads, should be dominated by considerations of safety. The paths should run in straight stretches and be clearly visible, with undergrowth kept well away. If possible they should be well lit at night.

70. A path through open woodland leads the visitor towards a remoter section with a lot of structural variety. Breda, Holland.

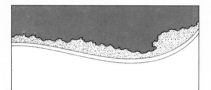

71a. A path skirting the edge of woodland continuously in open space.

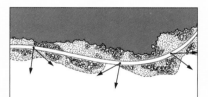

b. The woodland edge extends beyond the path which is partially hidden and is provided with views out to the open space at intervals.

72a A path running inside the woodland edge. Sutton Park, W Midlands.

b. A view from open space to the same path, hidden within a well developed edge.

73. Cycling through a heavily used wood needs careful management to avoid conflict. Here a separate cycle track solves potential problems. Amsterdamse Bos, Holland.

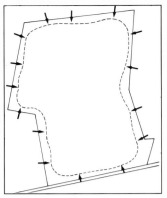
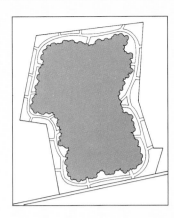

74a. A woodland area surrounded by housing or easy access and a multitude of possible ways in.
b. The perimeter path picks up all these access points and then controls further paths into the heart of the woodland.

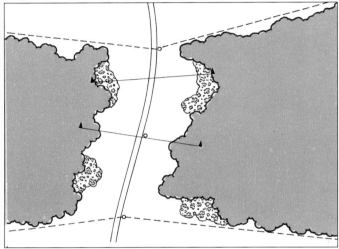

75a. Plan view of a path layout aimed at reducing the risk and fear of criminal attack. The route across the area can be seen at once, is well lit and the woodland edge kept well back.

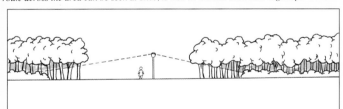

b. A section through the area where the street lamp reduces shadows beneath the trees.

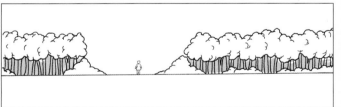

c. A section showing a gradual edge reducing hiding cover for would-be attackers.

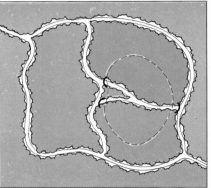

76. A combination of path routes means that some parts of the wood can be cordoned off during potentially dangerous operations such as tree felling while people are not prevented from walking circular loop paths elsewhere.

Recreation Space

Recreational use may range from organised formal sports, to informal picnicking or enjoying a rest in the course of a walk or short visit. Different sizes of open space, may be required from intimate and visually complex clearings to larger, more dramatic spaces. There will often be opportunities for contrast between places to stop and rest and those on a larger scale, which are experienced by moving though them.

77. Quiet contemplation of the woodland scene from a simple bench in a pleasant sunny glade.

Where an informal, natural-seeming space is desired, the area should be shaped to follow landform. Groups and clumps of trees and shrubs should be planted against the edge of the woodland. These groups may occupy up to a third of the open area, and subdivide the space into secluded, sunny bays for sitting and picnicking, or as sites for small structures such as toilets and information points. The clumps should be composed of two thirds of one species and the remainder of mixed species, especially smaller shrubby varieties to reduce the scale. Smaller groups or single trees out in the open space will add diversity. The surrounding woodland should be kept fairly open and well thinned, with a ground layer of woodland vegetation. Where bigger spaces are required for games, a central mown or grazed area can blend into the unmown edge, varied as described above.

More regular and managed spaces will contrast with more natural ones. If the former can be located so as to be a transition from the urban to the wild, the sense of escape may seem stronger.

78. A boisterous game of football underway in a large open space.

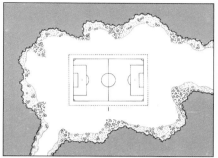

80. A formal games pitch may be laid out within an irregular space with detailed edge development.

81. Maintaining the scale of open spaces as trees grow:

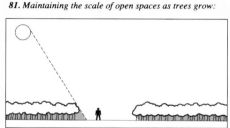

a. A young woodland where the sun reaches most of the open space.

b. As trees grow part of the space becomes shaded and the apparent scale reduces.

c. With more growth the space becomes more oppressive and almost completely shade.

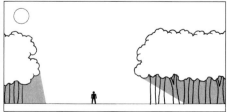

d. Substantial widening of the space is required to maintain the correct scale and the degree of sunlight reaching the ground.

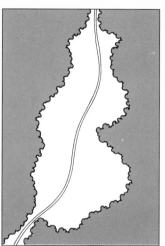

79a. Design for recreational purposes within a basic open space.

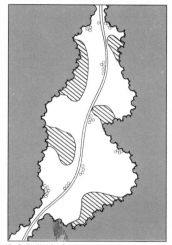

b. Sub-divide the open space by planting up to one third . This creates smaller areas where different groups of people can enjoy themselves without interfering with each other.

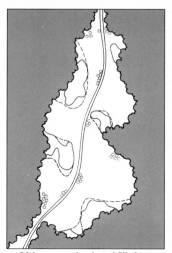

c. Of the areas to be planted fill about two-thirds with one species, to keep the unity of the design as simplicity of management.

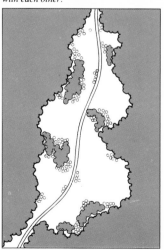

d. Of the remaining third, plant with a variety of trees and shrubs and good edge development and visual effect.

Other Glades

Other small open spaces may be needed around rocks, old trees or archaeological sites or other features so as to increase the drama of the setting. Others might serve as punctuation along paths or at path junctions. The smaller the space the more care is required in design especially in relation to proportion and sunlight.

Unless the layout is formal, such as avenues or visual axes, the edges of internal spaces should draw the eye easily from one part of the space to another, while emphasising any focal points. Width should vary, avoiding geometric or symmetrical shapes. Trees and shrubs placed within the space provide points of interest and can soften abrupt junctions of the vertical woodland edge with the plane of the ground.

The extent of open space around rocks and crags will depend on their size and importance as landscape features or geological sites. Leave sufficient space so that they are not obscured when trees are fully grown. These spaces should be designed in the same way as other forest shapes, with provision for access. If necessary seek advice from experts in the field.

Archaeological sites require similar treatment, following advice from a qualified archaeologist. Intervisibility from one site to another is sometimes helpful to give full meaning to each of them. Any corridors required for this should be designed as for other linear open spaces.

Views

Views are an important element in the design of open space, giving the viewer scenic variety and orientation. They must be identified in the appraisal survey . The design should aim to enhance the view, with trees in the foreground and middle ground providing a setting for the view rather than competing with it.

Views take a variety of forms, such as:

- **Panoramic views**, are seen from higher ground usually over steep slopes. They should have little restriction in the fore or middle ground. Any trees in the foreground should have a gently curving margin to underline the view. This is more effective than an abrupt frame.

- **Feature views** are dominated by one or a few eye-catching elements. Woodland design should draw the eye towards them.

- **Focal views** occur in valleys, with ridge lines directing the eye to the lower slopes. Overhanging trees can emphasise the point of convergence.

- **Canopied views** are those where the tree crowns form an overhead plane, and are best appreciated on foot. They can be developed over time by skilful management, and it is worth looking for possibilities for exploiting this device, particularly near recreation areas, albeit there may be many years to wait.

- **Filtered views** are seen through an open screen of foreground trees. The screen may be growing quickly and require frequent thinning, so this device should be employed with caution.

Views can become obscured requiring periodic work to keep them open. Encroaching vegetation may have to be removed or coppiced back, and trees pruned, thinned or felled as necessary. The immediate foreground must be left neat and tidy after these operations.

82. Types of view:

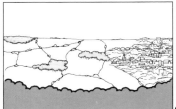

a. Panoramic view.

b. Feature view.

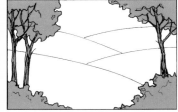

c. Focal view.

d. Canopied view.

e. Filtered view.

Power Lines and Service Corridors

In the changing landscapes near towns and cities it may not be clear how permanent are the routes of power lines. Extra lines may be required as new industry develops, or existing lines may be up-rated. Along with pipelines, they all require corridors of a certain width to be kept clear of trees. If new services are required after community woodlands have been established, may need to be put underground, given the effort and expense of organising, planning, designing and establishing these woodlands.

If planning authorities concede that power lines cannot be put underground, they and the woodland managers must insist that lines follow the least damaging route. Lines should always pass through open space, running alongside and not through woodland. They should also :

- avoid areas of landscape sensitivity;

- not follow the line of sight of important views;

- be kept in valleys and depressions;

- not divide a hill into two similar parts where they must cross over a summit;

- cross skylines or ridges where they dip to a low point;

- follow alignments diagonal to the contour;

- be inflected upwards in hollows and downwards on ridges.

Within the forest a power line should seem to pass through a series of irregular spaces. The forest should appear to meet across the open space in some places so that the corridor does not split the forest completely. A uniform width of corridor is not necessary even in operational terms. Trees can be planted closer to the line opposite pylons than in mid-span, where the line hangs lower and swings more. Smaller trees and shrubs can be grown closer still, as an extension of the forest edge towards the power line. This edge should have irregular spaces with irregular tree heights. Severe vertical edges, particularly of conifers, must be avoided.

The aim must be a corridor of varying character and width, the space swinging from one side of the line to the other; avoid irregular but parallel edges, or irregular but symmetrical spaces. Exit points should be gently asymmetrically bell-mouthed. Felling areas should be planned to link with and across the power line corridor to bring about greater irregularity.

Similar design considerations apply to pipelines and any other service corridors through the forest which have to be kept clear of trees.

83. A parallel-sided, narrow power line corridor cutting through a woodland area. Forest of Dean, Glous.

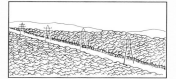

84a. A powerline corridor cuts through woodland with a straight, parallel sided swathe.

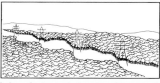

b. Introducing variation according to basic rules produces a symmetrical effect.

c. Analyse the landform using visual forces.

d. Design the corridor to interlock with the forest and follow landforms thus avoiding a parallel or symmetrical effect.

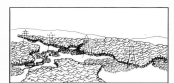

e. The persistent linear effect can be further broken by areas or groups of shrubs and coppice either increasing interlock further or breaking the line.

f. Linking the pylon corridor into other open spaces such as streams integrates it into the landscape further.

85a. A view inside a parallel-sided straight corridor is very boring and artificial.

b. The re-designed corridor is asymmetric with a well-developed edge structure. The sinuous space deflects the eye from the powerline.

Open Land Habitats

While the whole woodland should be designed to produce good wildlife habitats, there will often be opportunities to create new habitats in some of the open spaces. Whenever practicable they should be designed with education and public viewing in mind. They should look as natural as possible, perhaps by developing the natural character of existing habitats, and using the woodland edge and the shape of open space. **More detailed information on habitat potential, its development and management is available in "Nature Conservation in a Community Forest: Guidelines for Thames Chase", S. Marsh, Countryside Commission 1991 and "Nature Conservation and the New Lowland Forests", NCC 1991.** The following sections deal with particular design issues.

Deer glades are an example. Deer will establish themselves in any woodland which is relatively undisturbed, and can be encouraged to use glades where they can be viewed from hides. The glades should be shaped and edged to provide a natural-looking background, with sufficient shrubs for cover, fraying and browsing.

New Wetlands and Ponds

Bogs and wet areas can be formed by blocking existing drains or by judicious excavation. The plan shape should be irregular and asymmetric. Existing wet areas should be incorporated into the pattern where possible. The assessment of suitable sites, in both landscape and ecological terms, is an important part of the appraisal survey.

This applies equally to ponds. Existing wet areas are good sites for new ponds, always with the proviso that a rich wetland habitat must not be replaced by a poorer pond. Where there is clear wildlife value in constructing a pond, it should be sited where it might naturally occur, such as a low point in the landform, not perched halfway up a valley. This is also important if the water body and not the retaining dam is to be the dominant feature. Reflection, one of the chief visual benefits, is better when a pool is low down among trees and landform, with lateral light cut off. The spirit of the place should also be considered. A new pond could add to or detract from it, regardless of its value for wildlife.

Whether dammed or excavated, a pond must appear as natural as possible. The shape should incorporate bays, promontories and islands. If the pond is sufficiently large for parts of it to be hidden from view by islands and their vegetation, its apparent size will be greater and more interesting, as well as keeping parts more secluded and protected. Islands should be in scale with the surrounding landscape. If they have to be small they are best clustered and overlapped, to be viewed as a group. Islands can be safe nesting territory. Shallows and bays should ideally be south facing and overhanging trees avoided.

The underwater profile should replicate typical natural shapes, with some shallow and some steeper gradients so that aquatic and marginal vegetation can develop in its usual natural range. Ponds near children's play areas must be shallow and have a firm (preferably stoned) bottom and sides. This will reduce the potential wildlife values, but safety comes first.

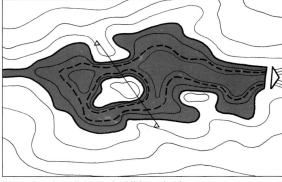

86a. A plan of a well designed wildlife pond with varying water depth, promontaries and an island which will remain cut off during lower water conditions.

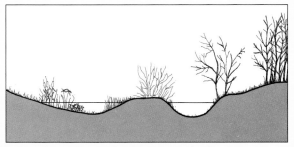

b. Section through the pond showing vegetation related to water depth and sunlight.

Where dams are proposed, obtain the advice of a qualified engineer on structural aspects. The dam should be shaped, wherever possible, to blend into the surrounding landform and be asymmetric in plan to avoid an artificial appearance. A dam wall of typical trapezoidal section will look out of place.

Fill material can be added to the basic engineered dam wall and the external face carefully graded to give a smooth blend with landform. Shallow-rooted shrubs planted on the added fill help to link the edge of the pond with surrounding vegetation. The inner face of the dam should also be made as natural as possible. Rip-rap (the large stones placed on the internal face of the dam to absorb wave energy and prevent erosion) should be irregular in appearance, and similar to locally occurring stone in colour and texture. Sluices and overflows should appear as natural streams, with rocks and stones laid irregularly, extending off the sluice to avoid a parallel edge.

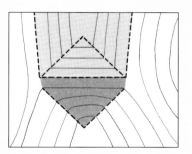

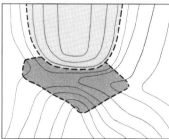

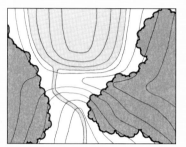

87a. Plan and view of a basic dam built to purely engineering specifications.

b. Adding fill to the basic dam enables it to be blended into the adjacent landforms.

c.With planting of shallow-rooted species on the added fill and a naturalistic overflow the final blending of the dam is achieved.

88a. An overflow to a pond which is highly artificial in appearance.

b. A similar overflow which appears more natural and which fulfils its function the same as (a.).

Woodland Rides

Rides are linear open spaces, often used for sporting or recreational access, and a traditional feature of lowland woodlands. Well designed rides are visually interesting and valuable open habitats. Their appearance is dominated by the forest edge. They should be of varying width, shape and direction, designed in response to landform like other internal open spaces. They should curve gently, with a succession of spaces of varying size through which the walker passes. The sequence should not be so complex as to disorient visitors.

The variety of habitats can be increased by setting back the forest edge to allow more sunlight to reach the ground, so benefiting vegetation and associated insects. The first step in design is laying out the edge shape. This should have 'bays' cut into the wooded area, irregularly spaced and varied in size, with backs not parallel to the ride. To avoid formality they should not be positioned opposite each other but should partially overlap.

89. The sequence of ride layout and design:-

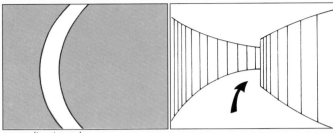

a. vary direction and ...

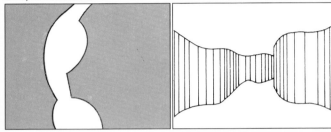

b. vary width but....

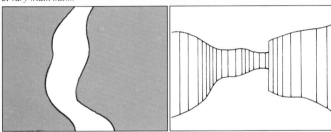

c. avoid symmetry and...

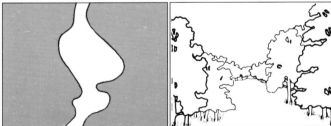

d. vary the scale of spaces and then ...

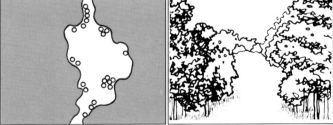

e. increase the diversity in the edge.

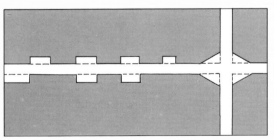

90a. The basic layout of bays cut into an existing edge or left unplanted can produce artificial effects.

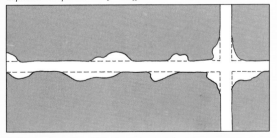

b. Curving bays of variable size and material produce a more natural appearance.

Having planned the edge shape, a path of mown grass can be designed, passing irregularly from one side of the ride to the other. Groups of broadleaved trees, tall and small shrubs and varied areas of rough grassland can be positioned and combined in an irregular interlocking pattern. Avoid parallel strips of trees, shrubs and grass. The ride system can be used to link other open spaces and form wildlife corridors, perhaps linking with features outside the woodland such as hedgerows and streamsides.

Do not lose sight of the access function of the rides. Though unsurfaced, they are particularly valuable in emergencies.

91. Improving or creating a ride design which is good for wildlife and walkers.

a. An existing parallel edge ride, or basic alignment.

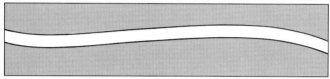

b. Shape the woodland edge to vary width and direction of spaces. Vary alignment of the path within the original ride.

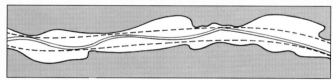

c. Decide where spaces need to be constricted or expanded to provide sequences, shelter or more sunlight. Use landforms where possible.

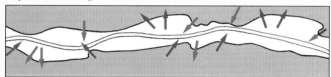

d. Emphasise construction of space to varying degrees by planting broadleaved trees and shrubs and emphasise expansion of space by heavy thinning and pruning of edges, or by lower density planting, where glades are wider. Add occasional groups where the path crosses an extensive space e.g. for more than 40 metres.

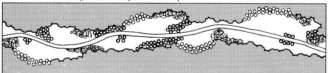

e. If greater conservation value or visual diversity is required residual areas may be managed as low shrubs or coppice with the remainder left as rough grass. Smaller alcoves, especially on the sunny side of the ride may be left and mown to provide areas for recreation.

92. The design of ride junctions

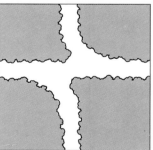

a. By aligning cross-junctions views can be terminated in two directions ...

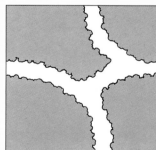

b. or all directions.

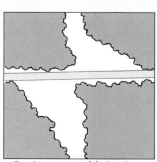

c. Opening out parts of the junction can terminate views (here shown at a road/ ride junction) and provide glades for conservation.

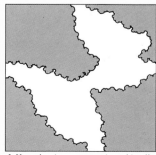

d. Here the views are terminated in all directions with glades for recreation or conservation also built in .

Hedgerows

If strong hedgerows are a prominent feature of the landscape, their interrelationship with woodland needs to be taken into account. Irregular distribution of trees along the hedgerows should be reflected and emphasised in the woodland edge. Any existing hedgerow trees in the woodland edge are of great value to landscape and wildlife and should be retained if practical. Adequate space should be left around their crowns to let them develop.

Where individual hedgerow trees are large, the loss of even a few trees has a major impact on the local landscape. The woodland edge should be planned so that younger groups of trees, growing in open conditions, can in due course be the successors to the present generation. It is difficult to match the irregularity of a mature hedgerow, with new planting so the diversity of the woodland edge should be exaggerated. The amount of irregularity in the hedgerow pattern in the vicinity of the wood, the general density of trees in the hedgerows and the variation in their spacing will be helpful guidance as to how woodland edge groups might be distributed.

Ancient hedgerows are of great historic and botanical interest, sometimes associated with ancient boundaries and often characterised by a wide range of tree and shrub species. It is important to recognise these survivals and to conserve their special features. Adequate space should be left on either side for light to reach ground level and to give them full scope to be appreciated as contributors to the spirit of the place.

93. The edge of the woodland and its relation to hedgerows and hedgerow trees.

a. Where the density of hedgerow trees beside the wood is typical of the surrounding landscape some outlying groups should be planted in between hedgerow trees of which a few should be replaced by planted groups to perpetuate the pattern.

b. Where there are fewer trees beside the wood, indentations in the edge and outlying groups should be used to enhance diversity.

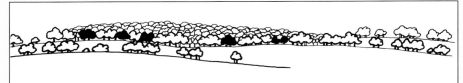

c. Where tree density is higher, selected groups of hedgerow trees should be felled and replanted in a pattern more typical of the surrounding hedgerows.

94. Old hedgerows with their associated flora form valuable features to be designed into the woodland. Here the hedges along this old lane are isolated relics in an otherwise highly altered landscape. Dagenham, Essex.

9. MINERAL WORKINGS
AND DERELICT LAND

Areas under consideration for community woodlands may include areas of derelict or disused industrial sites, storage areas, railway lines and sidings, opencast coal workings and deep-mine spoil heaps, sand and gravel pits and quarries. Some may be active, others reclaimed to a greater or lesser extent. The Local Planning Authority should always consider making planning consents for such activities within a community forest area conditional on subsequent restoration to woodland.

The effect on the end result may be great. It will often be the difference between achieving a vital landscape and being saddled with a visual liability. It will always be a dismal misuse of resources when ill thought out restoration has to be reworked either to improve the site conditions or the appearance.

Derelict Industrial Sites

Unless demolition and site clearance has been done to a high standard, the ground surface of these sites is likely to be severely compacted, even covered with concrete slabs and perhaps containing voids. Large solid materials should be removed or buried. The aim is to have surface layers which are fairly free draining, non-toxic and not too acid. Trees will grow in surprisingly impoverished materials as long as rooting is possible and water present but not stagnant. Some nutrients can be added if required. Toxic materials should be removed from the site. Brick, cement, crushed concrete and slag on railway yards or steel sites may be relatively alkaline and may give problems for tree growth.

Disused Railway Lines

Old railway lines seldom give difficulty and may already be colonised by woody vegetation. The track beds are useful for access routes, cycleways and the like. Tree growth and choice of species is not likely to be limited. Some old lines may act as useful reservoirs of various wildlife species to help colonise adjacent new woodland.

Opencast Coal Sites

Opencast working usually produces large areas of disturbed material at the surface, little of which can be called soil. In the past many of these areas have been reclaimed to agriculture, with a lot of effort put into the quality of the surface finish and drainage; this is not so important for a woodland end use. Deep drainage ditches and silt ponds can look very artificial and are serious barriers to recreation. Wherever possible adjust the profile of ditches and make ponds carry some water all year round, so that they look more natural and are better for wildlife. Landform is likely to be simple, so woodland planting may need to exaggerate it along margins. Providing large-scale water features allows the restorers to release additional spoil and to develop more emphatic landforms.

95. A deep drainage ditch on a restored opencast site. These form an artificial looking barrier to recreation. Walsall, W. Midlands.

96. A silt pond on a restored opencast site. With some imagination this feature could double as a conservation pond. Walsall, W Midlands.

97. A restored opencast area where open water and wetland has been created, greatly enhancing the conservation value of the area. Woorgreen, Forest of Dean, Glous.

Mineral Spoil Heaps

Many of the spoil heaps from deep mining have been reshaped and given back to agriculture. Where they have not yet been reclaimed this may be done to a specification suitable for woodland establishment. Landform has to be relatively simple and bland because stability and drainage are what matter.

Where sufficient land is avaliable the spoil heap can be spread and its form reworked to emulate the local natural contours. Where it must be reworked within its existing boundaries natural contouring may not be possible and a more emphatic approach, with deliberately more artificial landform, may be required.

In some areas deep mining is still producing sizeable spoil heaps. Ideally, tipping should of itself produce the desired landform rather than depending upon reworking. This requires that there be a clear view of subsequent use and a plan. This is necessary for planning permission. Computer terrain modelling can be useful in designing the woodland on the proposed landform shape. As parts of the tip are completed they can be planted in stages in accordance with the design for the whole. There may be substantial age differences between the areas planted at different times, so that each planting area must have an acceptable shape, reflecting landform and of a suitable scale.

98. A large deep mine coal spoil heap awaiting restoration or reclamation. New Herrington, Nr Sunderland, Tyne and Wear.

99. Designing woodland on reclaimed spoil heap.

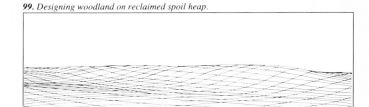

a. Computer simulation of landform to be created either by tipping or by reworking of existing spoil.

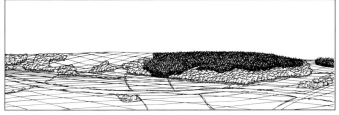

b. Woodland design carried out over the computer simulation.

Gravel Works

Substantial water bodies can result from gravel extraction. In the past many were not well shaped for subsequent use and reworking has been necessary. Pits can be worked to produce the desired shapes and profiles, so that minimal subsequent shaping is required before establishing the woodland and water edge.

    End uses of the site should be decided at the outset; these depend on location, eventual extent and shape. Recreation is one option, in the form of fishing, boating, windsurfing and water ski-ing. Wildlife conservation on the resulting water and wetland habitats is another. The two need not be incompatible, if correctly planned. Zoning is possible if the water area is large enough; if not, it is better to have several smaller lakes than one large one, so that different uses and activities are kept separate, with adequate buffer zones.

    Gravel extraction can be phased so that when work is completed on the first areas these can be planted. The woodland may then be developed before the whole site is worked out, so reducing the impact of gravel extraction on the environment, bearing in mind the timescale - up to 20 years or more - which is often involved.

    The design of the water areas and the woodland planting around the margins follows the lines described earlier for lakes and ponds. There must be provision for proposed end uses, such as access for boats.

100. An old gravel worked area where water and semi-natural vegetation have combined to produce a valuable habitat and interesting landform. Dagenham, Essex.

102a. A newly formed water area following sand and gravel extraction in Bramshill Forest, Surrey.

b. A similar site a few years later. Naturally colonising emergent vegetation is well developed.

101. The design of gravel working with an end use of mind

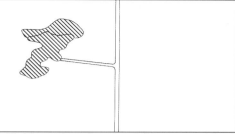

a. Work is started on a site at the end of the access road. Part is worked deeper than the rest and the plan shape is designed to be left behind with no further working.

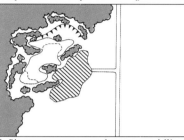

b. Phase two moves nearer the access road. Wet working is separated from phase one by a sand bar. Restoration and woodland planting can proceed on phase one.

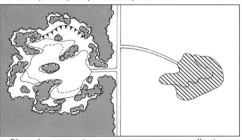

c. Phase three extraction starts on a separate area allowing phase two to be restored after the sand bar is removed leaving an island.

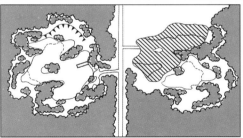

d. Phase four proceeds as phase two on the earlier site. Meanwhile recreational use is already happening on the restored areas from phase one and two.

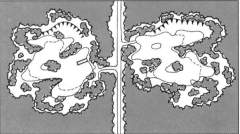

e. Phase five is the completion of restoration on the second site, this time with nature conservation in mind. Variable water depths, islands, promontaries and sand cliffs are left behind ready for planting and colonisation.

Quarries

Some areas have hard rock quarries, either active or abandoned. It is possible that new quarries may be started, though unlikely near built-up areas. Quarries can be unsightly and dangerous, but they can be reclaimed to different degrees. They may have a value as wildlife habitat or for recreation, in which case hazards such as high sheer faces, unstable slopes or water- filled holes must be rendered safe.

If the quarry is still active, the reserves can be assessed and its final appearance worked out, taking account of the safe height of the excavation and the reuse of waste materials. It is then possible to design the final shape to minimise reworking and expense.

The shape of the quarry face should reflect the landform, and the scale should be in keeping with that of the hill on which it is located. Any undisturbed area above the worked face should not be too thin, or parallel to the skyline. Breaking the skyline should be avoided wherever practicable. Shape should be asymmetrical. At the ends of the face, top soil or reshaped mounds of spoil with substantial planting can improve the scale in shorter views, and help to tie the quarry face into the surrounding landscape. Adding soil to suitable rock ledges will assist plants to colonise.

The shape of active quarries can be adjusted by extra excavation and by reworking spoil heaps to allow planting to take place. Blasting has been successful in limestone quarries as a means of forming scree slopes of more natural, safer profile.

Spoil heaps may be unstable, difficult to revegetate, and better left as scree. Elsewhere spoil should be reshaped, adding soil if necessary as a planting medium. Reshaping should be done in sympathy with the surrounding landform and planting to blend with existing woodland or other vegetation.

103a. A small quarry nearing the end of its life.

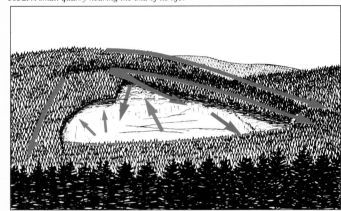

b. Visual appraisal to evaluate how its final working could be designed to produce a satisfactory end result.

c. The appearamce at the end of working with some vegetation restored or allowed to develop.

Refuse Disposal Sites

Many holes in the ground near towns have been used for refuse disposal. These sites cannot be built on afterwards and may become available as part of a community forest. Effective capping is necessary to seal off methane, which is inimical to tree growth. Extra overburden may have to be added to give trees adequate rooting depth.

Detailed guidance on techniques and choice of species for these sites is given in"A guide to the reclamation of mineral workings for forestry"(Forestry Commission, 1985).

10. DESIGN FOR INFORMAL RECREATION

A principal objective of community woodlands is the provision of locations for recreation opportunities close to where people live. Any necessary infrastructure and information must be looked at in terms of what visitors need throughout their visit. This will differ from place to place and can be accurately established only by survey. The following deals with the usual components of an informal recreation visit.

A visit starts in the mind of the visitor as he or she anticipates what is to come. This is as true of frequent visitors as of newcomers.

A high quality sense of arrival is of great moment in recreation design. Conversely a shabby entrance with inadequate signs or eyesores or inadequate management will give a first impression from which it is hard to recover. Signs must be unambiguous, well placed and relevant. Advance warning is important, especially on fast roads.

The entrance should be simple, clear, well signed and indicative of the high quality to come . Symbols are very helpful in conveying information quickly and elegantly, so long as they are understood.

A wind-down along a short stretch of road helps car drivers to readjust from the speed and anxiety of urban driving to the quiet and slower pace of the forest. This is a good start to the visit. The arrival at the car park, or other facility if walking or cycling, should confirm the good impression and the expectation built up over the journey. The design and layout of the car park or terminus, information, buildings and other structures must therefore be to a high standard.

104. High quality landscape along an approach road to a recreation area in woodland. Wendover Woods, Bucks.

105. A well designed entrance with a pleasant and inviting landscape and a well-positioned sign advertising the facilities available at the site. Salcey Forest, Northants.

106. The impression on arrival at the site must fulfil the expectations raised in the mind of the visitor. Here the diverse woodland edge, the sweep of the road and the well managed appearance provide a suitably favourable impression. Salcey Forest, Northants.

Car Park Design

A woodland parking area can usually afford to be reasonably spacious, in conscious contrast to the minimal space specification and large scale of most urban car parks. Instead of a mass of tightly parked cars, they can be split up into clusters of 3 to 7 cars along an access road, possibly on a one-way loop. Bays should be generous in size, any geometry in their shape being smoothed into curving edges. Bays beneath trees or out in the open, provide a choice of shade or sun.

107. Informal car parking bays sit amongst the trees provide a welcome contrast with urban layouts, inviting relaxation and a sense of quietness. Forest of Dean, Glous.

Some picnic places should be located close enough to the car park so that people can keep an eye on their car if they wish, yet allow children to run about without fear of accidents. A primary requirement is to separate pedestrians from vehicle circulation. Larger car parks can still use cluster parking but there must be a clearly defined circulation pattern especially if the car park has a one-way system or separate entrance and exit.

Theft from cars is a concern to many people. Keeping cars visible within the car park is a help, as are signs to remind people to lock up and take valuables with them. There is no evidence to suggest that casual thefts are any more common in woodland car parks than on the streets.

Materials should be chosen to be in keeping with the woodland surroundings. Roads with a gravel surface are preferable to tarmacadam. Where heavy wear causes high maintenance cost and a tarred surface is necessary, this should be finished with local coarse-textured gravel. Kerbs, white lines and other urban finishes are out of place: use simple bays, wooden posts or mounds and ditches to prevent cars being driven off the car park into the forest or on to open spaces.

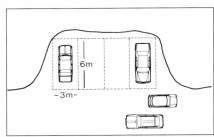

108. Car parking bay layout should be more generously proportioned than in an urban setting. The edge of the surfaced area follows an irregular curving shape which appears more natural.

109. The parking bay is surfaced with crushed stone but the road has been treated with a tar spray and chip finish to match. This helps prevent wear and tear on the running surface. Gortin Glen Forest Park, Ulster.

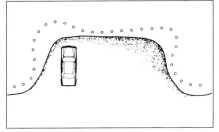

110a. Simple, stout wooden posts placed around the edge of a parking bay but not parallel with it, provide a useful, effective barrier to prevent cars driving on to picnic areas.

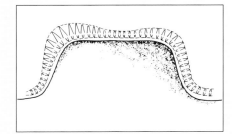

b. An earth mound blended into the surrounding contours is another useful traffic control device.

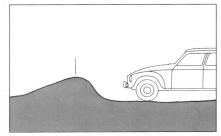

c. A section through an earth mound showing it steeper towards the car and gently blending into the surrounding contours away from it.

Footpaths, Bridlepaths and Cycleways

The layout and surfacing of pathways through woodland needs care, not least to avoid conflict between users. Bridlepaths are better designed to be completely separate from foot or cycle paths and with minimum crossing points. Junctions need good signing for horse riders, walkers and cyclists, with symbols instead of text. Whilst the footpath network may contain some steep and strenuous paths, a large proportion of the network should be accessible to wheelchairs, push-chairs and people with walking difficulties.

111. This area is well laid out with surfaced paths suitable for wheelchairs and pushchairs. The gentle gradient and smooth, firm surface are essential to allow complete access to all.

Curving, flowing alignments are preferred, without long straight stretches monotonous to walkers. Avoid steps, ramps and stiles as far as possible. Some paths can be left unsurfaced where there is light use; others will require surfacing with consolidated crushed stone. Lay this to a crowned profile, not a side fall which wheelchairs and push-chairs find difficult to negotiate. Sealed surfaces should only be considered for major through routes with heavy traffic, where water-bound surfaces would require too much maintenance. A spray and chip surface is preferable to heavy tarmacadam. Bridlepaths in clay soil areas may require surfacing with bark or some other types of litter.

112. A bridle path through woodland can often be churned up and difficult to maintain. Here sandy material provides a better surface in freely drained soils. On poor draining soils more complex surfacing of stone, geotextile and bark maybe needed to prevent degradation. Amsterdamse Bos, Holland.

Cyclists may be able to use old railway tracks as part of the access to a community forest. Road bicycles need good alignments and surfacing, while mountain bikes can use a much wider range of routes. On some soils heavy unrestricted use of mountain bikes can lead to the sort of surface damage associated with irresponsible horse riding and motor-cycling. These problems may require restrictions, provision of separate 'exciting' routes or circuits and zoning. If cycling use is very heavy, separate routes from walkers will be obligatory. Walking and cycling paths may be roughly parallel, separated by areas of trees and shrubs. Cycling surfaces should be compact and free from loose or sharp gravel soft patches and large protruding stones.

Path edges should be kept reasonably clear of tall vegetation and may need to be mown at intervals. The mown strip should not be parallel to the path but vary in width, as described above for woodland rides. Path drainage may be helped by simple devices such as grips across the path. These must be designed not to form traps for small wheels on wheelchairs or push-chairs.

Where a path crosses boggy ground the surface material can be supported on a mat of geotextile or branches, or boardwalks constructed. These should be made from sawn, treated timber and well maintained. A low edge will prevent wheels slipping off. A boardwalk beneath trees soon builds up a layer of slippery algal slime; plenty of light and good airflow keep the surface dry and with sufficient grip, without the need for wire mesh or similar devices.

Streams and ditches require culverts or bridges. Simple slabs of timber such as railway sleepers are sufficient for small crossings and rarely require handrails. Larger crossings need proper foot-bridges. **A suitable range of designs is contained in the book "Footbridges in the Countryside" (Reiach, Hall, Blyth, 1981).**

113. An inviting path leading through the woods. The simplicity of design and well maintained appearance do not detract from the surrounding landscape. The surface is well compacted and accessible to all users. Belvoir Park Forest, Belfast.

114. A well laid out boardwalk provides an interesting surface which protects the vegetation on the site. Pacific Rim National Park, British Columbia.

115. Drainage of paths is essential to prevent erosion and loss of surface material. Here a simple timber grip is adequate. These may cause problems for wheelchairs if the channel is too wide. Krimml, Austria.

Information Structures

Information and waymarking has been shown to be important to visitors, reassuring them that access is permitted and relieving them of anxiety of getting lost. This helps people to enjoy themselves and to get the most out of being in the forest.

The structures carrying information boards should be simple and robust, avoiding urban materials and designs. They should be chunky and in scale with the woodland. Timber in large sections, either round or sawn, is preferred. Avoid 'rustic' materials such as small irregular round timber with the bark left on; it is too suburban, and not durable. Round timber should be of good scale, low taper, regular dimensions and well treated with timber preservative. Dark or unobtrusuve coloured stains help reduce the impact of structures, emphasise the information and prevent the artefacts dominating the landscape.

Simple slabs of wood suffice for smaller signs; they can be set in the ground in a way which makes them difficult to remove. Recessed symbols and lettering, cut with a router, is a good technique to help reduce damage and vandalism. Waymarking of paths and trails should also be simple, using posts which can be replaced easily if damaged or removed.

Larger information signs should be positioned so as to be easily seen on arrival, oriented correctly, kept up to date and in good condition. Laminated panels set in a strong wooden frame with hidden fastenings are well proven over many years. Modern materials do not fade in sunlight and are not prone to degrade in wet conditions. Costly, complex structures requiring high maintenance should be avoided, as should structures with small roofs; these can look fussy and too urban or domestic.

116. A simple structure using well-scaled slabs of wood and laminated display panel providing well presented information. Bernwood Forest, Oxon.

117. Woodland traffic management signs, routed on slabs of wood provide a simple, non-urban alternative to metal signs. Wendover Woods, Bucks.

Children's Play

Children's play is likely to be an important activity in community forests, where the woodland environments have a great deal to offer for various types of play.

- **Physical activity play** designed for fitness, flexibility and general health; climbing, swings, slides, balancing poles and aerial ropeways are typical.

- **Social play** in which children learn to co-operate and to role play . Team games, activities in wendy houses and acting out stories are examples.

- **Educative play**, where children learn as they play. In the forest there are many ways to encourage children to learn, to become familiar with and to respect the environment. Play trails involving activities directly related to nature study are examples of this approach.

Facilities for play can range from standard types of structures, set in bark-surfaced areas and using landform, trees and water as special elements, to the forest as a whole with its naturally occurring materials, stones, dead wood, leaves and water.

118. Scrambling over this commando net provides enjoyable physical exercise as part of woodland play.

Play structures built around forest themes have also been successful. They may require design by a specialist sculptor to be really imaginative. Play trails based on forest animals - their homes, food and activities - are another possibility.

More detailed information is available in "Providing for children's play in the countryside", (Timothy Cochrane Associates for Countryside Commission for Scotland/ Forestry Commission 1984).

120. A play area at Grizedale Forest, Cumbria. where the equipment has been created by a sculptor and is based on forest animals.

119. These small children are learning something about their surroundings while enjoying their excursion to the woods. Water is always attractive! Aarhus, Denmark.

Small Buildings

Small buildings such as entrance kiosks, information centres, toilets and storage sheds are required at many recreation sites. These often look out of place if their form, material and scale contrast too strongly with the woodland.

The basic requirement is to get the scale right, especially the proportions of roof to walls. Use simple forms and materials, and finishes in keeping with the colours and textures of the woodland. Vertical spaced timber boarding, for example, echoes the texture of tree trunks. Profiled steel in dark grey or olive green adds coarse texture and visual weight to roofs, which is increased by a good overhang at the eaves. Avoid paint finishes on doors and windows - stains are less reflective and more easily maintained. Doors can often be accentuated by brighter colours such as reds or oranges. Bright greens are difficult to use as they clash with the natural greens of the woodland background.

Location of buildings is important. Place them against a backdrop of trees, to tie them into the landscape. Toilets and information buildings should be visible from the car park or arrival point, and their function indicated by symbol signs. Good visibility also aids their security. If they are only open seasonally they should have strong shutters over the windows.

Further information on the design and layout of toilet blocks is available in "Lavatories in the Countryside" (Reiach, Hall, Blyth for Countryside Commission for Scotland, 1985).

121. A woodland toilet block design which maintains a good scale and reflects the forest forms and textures in its materials and construction.

Small Structures

Gates, fences, picnic tables, benches, litter bins and other artefacts must be properly designed, if they are not to add clutter and fuss to a site.

Picnic tables are best positioned fairly near the car park, in bays among the vegetation. In areas further away and deeper in the forest, simple benches are better than the more formal picnic tables. Tables should be steady and level, and capable of use by people in wheelchairs.

Litter bins if necessary at all should not be too near picnic tables because of flies and wasps; nor should they be in the view, but placed at strategic points against vegetation on the access routes to and from the car park. Bins should be simple in design and easy to empty. Palisaded enclosures for standard black bin liners are one solution. Timber should be used if possible, even at the risk of fire.

Barbecue sites are popular and may take many forms. Low camp-fire styles give a more informal, wilder feel to the area than the typical patio barbecue. Free standing ones can be made demountable for winter storage. Firewood collection is not always desirable, especially in areas with wildlife conservation value, so it may be necessary to supply firewood.

Stock, rabbit or even deer fences may be necessary to protect newly planted areas. Gates and stiles in fences should be designed to allow people with disabilities to gain access. Allowing wheelchairs through but not motor cycles can be a real design problem; wheelchair kissing gates go some way to solving this, while remaining reasonably stock proof. **Design advice is available in the Countryside Commission Advisory Service Booklet No 15: "Informal Countryside Recreation for Disabled People".**

Gates, fences and stiles should be constructed simply and robustly from treated timber, either sawn or round, avoiding the rustic look. Sawn and round timber do not mix well. A high standard of maintenance is necessary to keep the number of all of these structures to a minimum.

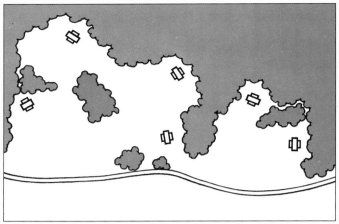

122. Diagrammatic layout of picnic tables around sunny bays set into the edge of the woodland.

123. In the forest a barbecue maybe informal and more like a camp fire. Here a low stone hearth and grill is all that is required.